ℙPLOUGHSHARES

Fall 2013 • Vol. 39, Nos. 2&3

GUEST EDITOR
Peter Ho Davies

EDITOR-IN-CHIEF
Ladette Randolph

MANAGING EDITOR
Andrea Martucci

FICTION EDITOR
Margot Livesey

POETRY EDITOR
John Skoyles

FOUNDING EDITOR
DeWitt Henry

FOUNDING PUBLISHER
Peter O'Malley

PRODUCTION MANAGER
Akshay Ahuja

EDITORIAL ASSISTANTS
Alexandra Artiano & Abby Travis

SENIOR READERS
Sarah Banse, David Goldstein,
& Abby Travis

INTERNS
Jessica Kent
& Jessica Slavin

COPY EDITOR
Carol Farash

BLOG EDITOR
Andrew Ladd

MARKETING ASSISTANT
Miriam Cook

ePUBLISHING CONSULTANT
John Rodzvilla

DIGITAL PUBL. ASSISTANTS
Jessica Arnold & Kathryn Deschamps

READERS
Jana Lee Balish | Doug Paul Case | Marlena Clark
Elisabeth Denison | Nicole DiCello | Jennifer Feinberg | Diana Filar
Colleen Fullin | Joshua Garstka | Bethany Gordon | Kristine Greive
Adam Hanover | Amanda Hartzell | Mark Hengstler | Eson Kim
Jordan Koluch | Karen Lonzo | Catherine Martin | Jean Mattes
Autumn McClintock | Caitlin McGill | Stephanie Mendoza
Marisela Navarro | June Rockefeller | Erin Salada | Charlotte Seley
Alessandra Siraco | Matt Socia | Kristen Winstead | Sonja Vitow
Charles Walker | Caitlin Walls | Leah Welch | Caitlin White

ADVISORY BOARD
William H. Berman | DeWitt Henry | Alice Hoffman | Ann Leary
Tom Martin | Pam Painter | Janet Silver | Daniel Tobin | Marillyn Zacharis

Ploughshares, a journal of new writing, is guest-edited serially by prominent writers who explore different personal visions, aesthetics, and literary circles. *Ploughshares* is published in April, August, and December at Emerson College 120 Boylston Street, Boston, MA 02116-4624. Telephone: (617) 824-3757. Web address: pshares.org. E-mail: pshares@pshares.org.

Advisory Editors: Sherman Alexie, Russell Banks, Andrea Barrett, Charles Baxter, Ann Beattie, Madison Smartt Bell, Anne Bernays, Frank Bidart, Amy Bloom, Robert Boswell, Henry Bromell, Rosellen Brown, Ron Carlson, James Carroll, David Daniel, Madeline DeFrees, Mark Doty, Rita Dove, Stuart Dybek, Cornelius Eady, Martín Espada, B. H. Fairchild, Nick Flynn, Carolyn Forché, Richard Ford, George Garrett, Lorrie Goldensohn, Mary Gordon, Jorie Graham, David Gullette, Marilyn Hacker, Donald Hall, Patricia Hampl, Joy Harjo, Kathryn Harrison, Stratis Haviaras, Terrance Hayes, DeWitt Henry, Edward Hirsch, Jane Hirshfield, Tony Hoagland, Alice Hoffman, Fanny Howe, Marie Howe, Major Jackson, Gish Jen, Justin Kaplan, Bill Knott, Yusef Komunyakaa, Maxine Kumin, Don Lee, Philip Levine, Margot Livesey, Thomas Lux, Gail Mazur, Campbell McGrath, Heather McHugh, James Alan McPherson, Sue Miller, Lorrie Moore, Paul Muldoon, Antonya Nelson, Jay Neugeboren, Howard Norman, Tim O'Brien, Joyce Peseroff, Carl Phillips, Jayne Anne Phillips, Robert Pinsky, Alberto Ríos, Lloyd Schwartz, Jim Shepard, Jane Shore, Charles Simic, Gary Soto, Elizabeth Spires, David St. John, Maura Stanton, Gerald Stern, Mark Strand, Elizabeth Strout, Christopher Tilghman, Richard Tillinghast, Colm Tóibín, Chase Twichell, Jean Valentine, Fred Viebahn, Ellen Bryant Voigt, Dan Wakefield, Derek Walcott, Rosanna Warren, Alan Williamson, Eleanor Wilner, Tobias Wolff, C. D. Wright, Al Young, Kevin Young

Subscriptions (ISSN 0048-4474): $30 for one year (3 issues), $50 for two years (6 issues); $39 a year for institutions. Add $30 a year for international postage ($10 for Canada).

Upcoming: Winter 2013-14, a staff-edited poetry and prose issue, will be published in December 2013. Spring 2014, a poetry and prose issue edited by Jean Thompson, will be published in April. Fall 2014, a fiction issue edited by Percival Everett, will be published in August.

Submissions: The regular reading period is from June 1 to January 15 (postmark and online dates). All submissions sent from January 16 to May 31 will be returned unread. From March 1 to May 15, we also read for our Emerging Writer's Contest. Please see page 185 for editorial and submission policies, or visit our website: pshares.org/submit.

Back-issue, classroom-adoption, and bulk orders may be placed directly through *Ploughshares*. *Ploughshares* is also available as full-text products from EBSCO, H. W. Wilson, JSTOR, ProQuest, and the Gale Group. Indexed in M.L.A. Bibliography, Humanities International Index, Book Review Index. Full publishers' index is online at pshares.org. The views and opinions expressed in this journal are solely those of the authors. All rights for individual works revert to the authors upon publication. *Ploughshares* receives support from the National Endowment for the Arts and the Massachusetts Cultural Council.

Retail distribution by Ingram Periodicals, Media Solutions, Ubiquity, and Disticor Direct in Canada. Printed in the U.S.A. by The Sheridan Press.

NATIONAL
ENDOWMENT
FOR THE ARTS

massculturalcouncil.org

CONTENTS

Fall 2013

Cover: Pat de Groot, *Cormorant Drying Its Wings*, 1991, Sharpie marker on cotton charcoal paper, 18" x 12". Drawn from life on a kayak at the Provincetown breakwater. Used by permission of the artist.

PETER HO DAVIES
My Share

It must seem an odd—even disqualifying—admission in an editor, even a guest editor, but I don't really like to judge fiction, though that hasn't stopped me doing so for *Ploughshares,* or in the past (not least each winter when I, along with my colleagues, read several hundred MFA applications). On reflection, my unease is less about judging than *being* judged. Judge not, as the gospel warns us, lest ye be judged. While my professional life has provided plenty of opportunities to second guess my own judgment—the rejected candidate, say, whose book went on to sell millions of copies—I suspect most of us feel a similar anxiety about our judgment, or to use another word, our taste. It's what underlies that flash of indignation when we disagree with the prize committee for this year's Pulitzer, or that year's National Book Award. Why we throw up our hands at the decisions of Nobel or Booker or Oscar voters. We're enraged by their flawed judgments, by the injustice of it all, but part of our outrage is surely fueled by self-doubt. Those panels are judging the works and artists before them, but also obliquely *our* tastes, implicitly approving them if we agree, disparaging them if we diverge. *How dare they! Who do they think they are!* (The very fury that fuels the familiar countercharges of judicial elitism, or cronyism, political correctness, or populism.) In my own case, this readerly anxiety is reflected and magnified in writerly paranoia: if my judgment is suspect, how can I rely on my judgment of my *own* work? But I suspect it may be traced back even further, like so much that is traumatic, to high school. I can still remember shyly declaring a passion for some band or other only to be ridiculed by my peers. I can't recall a similar instance where I was mocked for liking a particular book, but that's probably because I never made such a confession—merely liking books, *any* book, being grounds for derision at that age.

Is this why we're so intent on best-seller lists, and prizes? For all that we might dispute the latter, there's also safety in such imprimaturs, a safety in numbers. The way we congregate as readers around genres may also have roots in this pack mentality. If everyone's reading it, it must be OK. We don't have to expose our own judgment if we follow others. *Oh, that? Yeah, my book group/Oprah/my professor picked that.* But lately, I've come to wonder if there isn't another, perhaps more positive reason for this anxiety of judging. Having one's opinion questioned shouldn't be daunting so long as one can defend it, after all. And yet, I hesitate to offer such a defense, to explain why I picked something. Oh, I can put on a decent show if pressed, as teaching sometimes obliges me to do, but anyone who's taught literature knows that it's often painful to teach a text you love. It's disappointing when students don't love it (that old high-school anxiety writ large) and frustrating in that it's often difficult, even painful, to explain *why* we love what we love. The key word here, of course, is *love*. It's impossible to explain why we love, to reduce the irreducible. Explanation belongs in the realm of the rational. Love is something else—in life as in literature—and it transcends (for good and ill) judgment. I'm not religious in the least, but it's hard to escape the notion that this is precisely the break the New Testament makes with the Old.

Finally, I'm reminded here of that common question asked of writers in interviews or Q&As after readings, sometimes phrased "What books do you recommend?" or even more chillingly, "What's your favorite book?" I have stock answers/evasions now, after too many instances of deer-in-the-headlights paralysis (panicked by choice, I'm apt to forget every book I've ever read) and on one occasion a flat-out boorish refusal to answer. But beneath my panic lies a surprising truth. I don't actually *want* to disclose these titles, and not (only) for fear of being judged. It's because I don't want to share what I love.

At first glance this seems a strange selfishness. Books are mass produced objects, after all, there are plenty of copies to go around. But a love of them implies something more rarefied—*intimacy.* We feel an intimate connection to a book we love, more personal even than the connection we feel to favorite movies or music, which we often encounter in actual or strongly implied groups—at a theater, a concert, as a member of a mass TV or radio audience. Books, by contrast, we read alone (even if we read them for a class or a book group, we read them alone, at our own pace, pausing where we will). Or rather, not alone, but in the ghostly company of others—the characters, and the author. A movie may be funnier or more exciting if viewed in a crowded theater, a song more euphoric if experienced on a dance floor, but a book is enhanced by this intimacy. And intimacy is in some sense inimical to sharing. My relationship with my wife is precious by virtue of its exclusivity. Similarly my relationship with a book or a story is precious because it feels unique, as if no one else might understand that work or that author in quite the same way. (A best seller, a prizewinner, enjoyed and admired by many is perhaps less likely to offer this quality, unless we find in it something we think that all those other readers missed.) Intimacy, by these lights, is the ultimate elitism. Never mind that it might be illusory—what is fiction, after all, if not illusory? And this is the thrill I found in each of these stories: the sense that they spoke to me alone. That's what made me fall in love with them. And perhaps it's what underlies my anxiety about judging: not that you might dispute my judgment, but that you might share it. An even odder admission in an editor, I think you'll agree, though perhaps an apposite one given that the word *share* has an etymological root in common with the word *shear,* as this very journal's name reminds us. To share something is first to shear it; it must be cut and divided before it can be parceled out. To share is thus at once to keep and to give.

Tell Me My Name

Ever since the California economy collapsed, people have been coming
to our street at night and going through the trash. That sounds worse
than it is—I guess if it's recyclable, then it's not really trash. They sort
through the blue bins that were wheeled out to the curb during the
day by the gardening crews. The people who come at night are like a
crew too. You used to see just the solo collectors, but over the past few
months they seem to have joined forces. They're efficient, with one of
them holding onto the grocery cart and organizing things while the
others pull out bottles from the bins. At first, they carried flashlights,
but now they wear headlamps.

My neighbor Betti isn't happy about the situation. She stands on my
porch, waving her extra-sharp tweezers in the air. She came over with
a splinter lodged under her fingernail, and after a little poking around,
I got it out. It's the middle of the afternoon but she knew I'd be home.
Now that the splinter is gone she's free to be irritated by other things,
and my trashcans, lined up at the curb, have started her thinking about
the recyclers. "I moved here to get away from this shit," she says, and
even though she talks in kind of an ugly way, Betti is one of the most
beautiful people I know.

She has arching eyebrows and the smallest possible pores, flat red
lipstick that never rubs off on her teeth or crumbs up in the corners
of her mouth. Shining dark hair smoothed back in a high ponytail.
Toreador pants and little ballet flats so silvery and supple I hate to see
them touching the sidewalk. The math still shocks me: she must be at least
forty-five years old! You'd never know it, because her skin is amazing.

I used to look at her picture in magazines, ages ago, when I was a
regular girl going to middle school and she was a popular person going
to gay dance clubs in New York. Her friends were graffiti artists, punk
bands, drag queens, rappers, gallery owners: everything was all mixed
up then, in a good way. I used to read those magazines monkishly,
over and over again, late into the night, as if they contained a key to
unlocking a secret world of happiness. And maybe they did; maybe
they taught me something important. Or maybe it was just a way to

kill time until I could grow up, get a job, find a partner, buy a house—
A house four doors down from Betti Pérez! The houses are small but they cost a lot. What I mean is that they look sweet on the outside but there may be comedians or talent managers or people like Betti living inside.

"The other morning, I'm standing in my kitchen," she says, "still in my nightie, trying to get the toaster to work, and I hear something funny. A rustling around kind of sound, like a rat makes? And I look over and there's a little man right outside my pantry window! Ten feet away from me! Digging away in there, helping himself."

"You should get your gate fixed," I tell her.

She raises her black eyebrows at me. "Don't make this my fault."

"Secure the perimeter, that's what Officer Cordova said."

"I'm trying to tell you a story."

"Didn't I give you Manuel's number?"

Betti scowls. "I'm going to get mad if you don't stop busting my balls."

A wave of happiness rushes over me. Here I am, fussing at Betti Pérez, and here she is, fussing back at me. I want to reach through time and squeeze the arm of my thirteen-year-old self: awake at one in the morning, sucking on Altoids, studying the captions in PAPER magazine...

Betti doesn't know that I liked her back when she was an underground queen of New York. She probably thinks I've seen her on the HBO show, or remember her from that recurring role on the one about the lawyers. The fact is, I don't watch too much TV, but there's no way I can say that around here without sounding ungracious.

"I wasn't wearing any panties," she says, suddenly thoughtful. "It made me feel sort of frozen in place. Like one of those bad dreams where you can't move your legs and you open your mouth but no words come out. The only thing I could do was grab my phone off the counter and shake it at him."

I tell her that the next time, she should grab her phone and call Officer Cordova.

"The point is, they're not waiting for trash day anymore," Betti says. "The point is, they're *encroaching*."

On cue, my dog starts barking crazily from behind the picture window, as if he knows exactly what *encroaching* means. He's a big dog and his bark is loud, fast, and desperate. Though I've been living with him for over a year, his thinking remains mostly mysterious to me. I apologize to Betti and we look at my dog making a steady stream of sound, the wetness from his mouth spraying onto the glass. "Quiet, Hank," I say, but he ignores me, which isn't unusual for us. Betti says she has to leave. She's informed me before that when he barks, it's clearly audible at her house, even with her music on.

"Tell Amy I'm still waiting to hear from her," she says, leveling the tweezers at me, then she pivots on her soft silver shoes and walks away.

When I go back inside, my dog is lying attentively on the carpet, cheerful and calm, as if he truly has no idea who that maniac was, barking his head off.

I should say *our* dog not *my* dog because Amy and I adopted him together. We biked to the farmers' market one morning to buy some strawberries and salt and eggs and came home instead with a dog; they told us he was a shepherd mix, but I suspect he's more mix than shepherd. The various rescue organizations are clever and set up shop all along the sidewalks on Sundays, so you can't buy a muffin or pick up your prescription without encountering at least a dozen beautiful animals needing homes. It's like running the gauntlet except instead of being pummeled with sticks, you're pierced by the sad eyes of kittens and stray dogs, and the less expressive eyes of rabbits. There are always a couple of weeping children too, who want the animals but can't have them.

I wanted a child but couldn't have one, which is partly why we got the dog. Or maybe the dog is our warm-up to having a child—this is how Amy, who is plucky about nearly everything, looks at it. I'm the defeatist. I think the game's already over. I think of Hank as a consolation prize, a loud and needy consolation prize who sheds huge amounts of hair, but that could just be the hCG. Now that we've started on injectable cycles I've been feeling blue. "Get out," Amy tells me. "Take Hank for a hike." Which always seems like a reasonable idea until I try to execute it. Amy says that the problem is my car; if I had a bigger car, it wouldn't be such a major production. She's been researching hybrid SUVs and threatening to take me on a test drive.

As for me, I don't want a bigger car. I miss the days when we didn't even own a car. I mean before we came to California, when we were still working crummy day jobs and living in New York. It used to take me twelve minutes to walk to the C/E station from our apartment on DeKalb. I used to bury my nose in my scarf and finger the smooth, flimsy MetroCard in my coat pocket and think about the magazine I would read once I got a seat on the train. Usually I would read for only a few minutes before I fell asleep, lulled by the shaking train and the warmth of other people around me reading and sleeping. If I had to get to work early, I would walk the extra distance and take the D/Q line from Flatbush Avenue, just because I looked forward to the moment when the train emerged from the darkness to make its slow, rattling way across the bridge and the morning light would pour slantwise through the girders and spill over all of us sleeping inside the subway car, our hands folded and our heads nodding, me cracking my eyes open for only a second to see this and love this and then go back to dreaming.

The next time Betti appears on my porch she is holding a blue ice pack on top of her head. The rest of her is perfect: jersey wrap dress in navy, big gold hoops, long gold chains looped around her neck. She says, perfectly matter-of-fact, that she needs me to see if she is bleeding.

"Should I take you to the hospital?" I ask, trying to keep Hank from wriggling past me and out the door. With all my blood tests, I go to the hospital like a regular. "I know a great place to park."

"It's only a bump," Betti says. "I bumped my head like an idiot. You better get some hydrogen peroxide, just in case."

I find it in the downstairs bathroom, along with a little plastic packet containing two quilted cotton pads that Amy must have taken from a fancy hotel. I think that Betti will like how neat and individually wrapped they are. She sits on the lower step of the porch and I sit on the higher one, leafing through her hair. She's released it from its ponytail.

"I don't even want to tell you how it happened. It's stupid, fucking stupid, and it's going to make me mad all over again."

But of course she tells me. She tells me that the little man came back. He startled her when she was wiping something off the kitchen floor, and she stood up too quickly and banged her head on the corner of an open cabinet door.

"Really hard," she says. "I could practically see the stars and tweetie birds flying around. I did that concussion test, the one where you close your eyes and touch your nose. I'm OK in that regard."

I can't find a scratch anywhere. Just pale, clean scalp and the dark roots of her hair. I can see where she hit it, because the skin is pinker there and cold from the ice. But no blood. I split open the plastic packet and unscrew the cap from the bottle of peroxide. When I touch the wet pad to her head, Betti sighs with pleasure.

"Oh boy. I feel like I'm in the nurse's office at school. She used to go through our hair checking for lice. Every week, with her rubber gloves and a cotton ball soaked in alcohol."

She laughs. "See? I told you I'm from the ghetto. That's what Catholic school was like in the Bronx. Back in the day!"

I love her so much. I don't even bother to ask if she has Manuel's number. I'm just going to call him myself, like I did when her sprinklers were flooding the sidewalk. No more recyclers breezing through her broken gate.

"Is it bad?" she asks soberly. "Is it deep?"

"It's nothing to worry about," I say, and smooth my hands over her shining hair.

"Thank you, bunny," she says, placing her ice pack back on her head, but now at an angle, like a beret. "It's hard living alone sometimes."

I know how she feels, even though technically I'm not living alone. Betti and her husband Rick split up over a year ago. He's a contractor, with a show on a cable network where he rescues people from home improvement projects that have gone terribly wrong. It's called *D.I.Y. Undone*. It's funny because D.I.Y. used to mean something positive to me; it meant publishing your own magazine or starting a record label or making documentaries on borrowed cameras about homeless LGBT teenagers living in Morningside Park. Now D.I.Y. just makes me think of Rick and the look of relief on homeowners' faces when he pulls up in his vintage pickup truck. On the show, he is heroically competent, but I've noticed that a lot of things at Betti's house don't work as well as they should, like the gate. He redid the whole house himself as a wedding present to her.

"You want to come inside?" I ask. "Everything's a mess."

Betti stands and studies Hank through the picture window, as if calculating how many dog hairs are going to attach themselves to her navy dress. "I've got a meeting. A big one, maybe. In Santa Monica."

I knock my knuckles against the nearest porch column. "I think this is wood."

"Speaking of which," Betti continues, "has Amy said anything to you? I feel like I'm stalking her."

"Not yet." I wasn't expecting this, and now I have to pretend to sort through the contents of our mailbox. "She's super busy. Even more than normal. She hasn't even had time to do her laundry." Which doesn't sound very convincing, so I hear myself adding: "There's a huge pile of unwashed clothes stinking up the back of the closet."

I don't know why I offer up this detail; why, in my panicked effort to make another person feel better, I always end up exposing Amy in an exaggerated and totally unnecessary way. The sickness I feel afterward somehow doesn't stop me from witlessly doing it again. Her adult ADD, her iffy eating habits, her dirty clothes...

Betti looks away, embarrassed—for Amy? For me? "She's seen my work, right?" Oh! For herself, and it makes me want to hold her hand. "You think I should tell my agent to send over some DVDs?"

"No! Don't. We're really big fans." My voice gets a little throaty from the relief of finally saying it. And it doesn't seem wrong in the moment to say we, even though I'm actually just speaking for myself. "We love you. We've loved you forever."

"Seriously?" Betti asks. She smiles, her face opening. Everything about her softens a little. "You guys. You kill me."

"Like, forever."

We grin at each other. I want to tell her that she's the reason I moved to New York.

"So you get why this is such a good idea," she says, before I have my chance. She removes the ice pack from her head and leans in as if she's telling me something new. "It's a no-brainer. It's my retirement fund."

For a while she's been wanting to pitch a kids' show to Amy, because that's what Amy makes: half-hour television shows for kids. And that's how we get to live in this house! To be clear, Amy's show is not the educational kind, more like the kind that parents complain about, but the writing is smart and these kids are lovely to watch, bright-eyed and funny and quick. Real actors, grown up now, with serious careers, have gotten their start on this kind of show. What I'm trying to say is that it's not dreck, and Amy turns out to be very talented at it, even though it's given her sciatica and a sleeping disorder. How does a slightly graying lesbian documentary maker know exactly what 8- to 12-year-old girls will enjoy watching while curled up in their beanbags, eating snacks? "It's my uncanny ability," Amy likes to say, half joking and half amazed. But we're just like those girls; we've always been interested in teenagers too, so maybe it's not such a leap after all.

In Betti's show there'll be two teenagers—the finicky older brother and the gorgeous, unmanageable sister—and then a couple of younger siblings thrown in for laughs and relatability. Betti's plan is that one of the little ones will be an adopted kid from Asia or Africa. Or even better, both of them could be adopted! But definitely from different continents. Anyway, four kids at the very least, though she's open to more. And an uptight, standoffish dad—think Captain von Trapp as a captain of industry—plus probably one more adult for good measure: a Scottish housekeeper with fluffy hair? a fluty-voiced building manager? Someone to balance out Betti—because the whole idea is that Betti's character isn't really an adult. She's the wildly inappropriate babysitter.

Former denizen of downtown clubs, former b-girl, former hair-dresser, former bad girl from the Bronx, with the accent to boot: Guess who's taking care of the kids! She's faked her résumé; she has no business doing this; all she's got is a tube of Chanel lipstick and her street smarts. When they push her, she'll push back. Sass, life lessons, more sass. Thrift store shopping, gum snapping, wisecrack-ing, pop and locking. In the pilot, she'll enter the little ones in a city-wide dance contest.

It makes sense, I can see that. I can see the appeal. Objectively, it's not sillier or more overcooked than any other show on Amy's network. But the idea of Betti pausing for a laugh track still makes me more depressed than I can say.

She reminds me that the concept has already been done, which is apparently what makes it such a sure bet now. "That went for six full seasons," she says, "and ended a decade ago. It's way overdue for a relaunch." She hoots to hear herself talking this way. "Jesus Christ! I sound like my fucking manager."

"He isn't concerned," I ask, "about going in a different direction? Because the stuff Amy does, it's not exactly—"

"My manager? Please! He'll pimp me out for any old thing." Betti gives me her ice pack so she can use both of her hands as she's talking. "And so what if it's not high art? I did that. I made those movies. I love independent film as much as the next girl. The first film I ever did?

It went to Cannes and came *this* close to winning a Palme d'Or. So what have I got to prove? I like working. I like making money. I've got a mother who I want to take care of. Is Rick still paying the mortgage on that house? I don't think so. And most people don't know this, but HBO residuals are shit. So what, this show's not going to Cannes. You want to criticize me for trying to get my hustle on? Fuck you. Someone's got to pay my bills."

I think I must look a little stunned, because Betti touches my arm. "Oh bunny, I didn't mean *you*. It's just a colorful expression."

"I know that," I tell her. "I say it sometimes for emphasis too."

"You're funny." Betti shakes her head and descends the steps, sending a goodbye wave over her shoulder. "Now all we have to do is come up with a name." She looks back at me as if she's not sure I've been keeping up with her. "For the show!"

It's two days later when Manuel rings the doorbell. His white truck is in the driveway, its bed stacked with cedar planks. After saying hello, I point down the street. "It's Betti's gate," I remind him, "not ours."

"Surprise!" He laughs softly. "I'm here for *you*." I notice how young he looks with his new haircut, and I notice the pleasant, artificial scent of laundry soap that his shirts always let off at the beginning of the day. If we lived in New York, and I had taken a seat next to him on the subway, I might have fallen asleep on his shoulder.

He keeps patting his front pocket, even though his cell phone isn't in there. He tells me that he's going to build a chicken coop in my backyard.

I can't help repeating it. "A chicken coop? In our yard?"

But he's already back by his truck, hoisting planks onto his shoulder.

"Is this Amy's idea?" I call out.

He nods, which is difficult to do with all the wood that he's balancing. "She wants to give you a surprise."

"I didn't think Amy even had your number," I say pointlessly. I'm still trying to get my bearings. "You talked about where she wants to put it?" I ask as I follow him down the driveway.

Without grunting, he deposits the first load onto the grass. "I think you'll like it," he says. When he straightens, he pauses for a moment, then smiles. "The dog is quiet today."

It's true. Hank is miraculously silent. Usually he goes bonkers whenever Manuel or any other male sets foot on the porch, or the driveway, or especially when someone dares to venture into the backyard. "He's getting to know you," I say brightly, but I am disturbed. His insane barking is what reminds me that Hank has a past, and memories from a time before we knew him. I can't understand why he is now soundlessly watching us through the glass of the back door.

Manuel says that the coop will be big enough to hold six chickens. "That's many eggs," he observes, and I inwardly sicken, and it occurs to me then that neither he nor Amy has any idea what a bad, bad joke this whole urban agrarian cedarwood surprise is. I gaze at him dumbly as he digs his little dowels into the ground and then uses string to mark off the dimensions of the chicken structure. I know Manuel is just doing what Amy asked him to do, and I know Amy is just trying to keep me balanced and upbeat, but think about it: while she's out in Burbank making kids' shows, and the chickens are out in the backyard making eggs, I'll be in the kitchen making rosemary cookies to bring as a gift to my reproductive endocrinologist. Sometimes, as I'm sanding the cookies with granulated sugar or sticking myself in the stomach with a disposable needle, it's hard to remember that I used to make other things, and who cares if in the end they never found distribution, I made them, Amy and I made them together.

"Knock knock," says a voice coming down the driveway, a voice so recognizable that Betti has wondered aloud on occasion why she doesn't yet have a voice-over career. "What are you kids doing back here? I saw the truck."

Betti's shoes are very pointy in the toes and high in the heels, so she can't step onto the grass to take a closer look at the construction site. "Where the heck do you get the chickens from?" she asks.

"I have no idea." I sink into a stackable chair left over from our last cookout. "Though I imagine Amy already has somebody working on it."

I say it so dryly that I surprise myself.

"You be nice!" Betti says, aiming a tapered red fingernail at me. "I finally got a meeting with her. Next Monday, and I'm a fucking nervous wreck, and I couldn't have done it without you."

She dips her hand wrist-deep into her purse and delicately shifts things around until her hand reappears, flourishing a business card. "I'm giving you a session with my acupuncturist. He's going to seriously help you. He says no more cold drinks. No ice cream." She passes me the card and heads for my back door. "You got to keep everything nice and warm in there. OK? Like a greenhouse. Don't move; I'm getting you a cup of hot water."

To her credit, Betti opens the door only a crack and inches herself through sideways, but Hank is fast and unfathomable, and after all that weird stillness and silence at the back door, he now squirms past her and comes hurtling out into the yard. Manuel and I freeze. The last time this happened it was bad; Manuel said afterward that it was OK, it was just the edge of his shirt, an old shirt, but I'm not so sure I believe him. I was straddling Hank and gripping his choke collar, and both the dog and I were panting. I don't think Manuel told me everything in that moment, and I failed to ask him about it again. But today Hank goes right past him, past the cedar planks, past the paloverde tree and the big bank of native grasses, straight down to the fence, where he begins to sniff about with a frantic sort of urgency.

"I was nervous there for a second," I say, half-laughing, ashamed. "My fault!" Betti calls from behind us. "Everyone OK?" Without comment, Manuel stands formally and adjusts his position so that he can keep his eye on the dog as he works.

I watch Hank patrol the fence, his nose to the ground, snuffling in and around the wood chips. When we first had the plantings installed, we thought Hank was chewing on the leaves and making himself sick. While walking across our new yard, Amy and I would find large puddles of vomit sitting neatly on top of the mulch. We decided we had to keep Hank shut inside, we had to live with his miserable yelping and barking and door-scratching, me more than Amy because I'm the one who's at home with him, and still we continued to wake up and find the foamy yellow pools scattered among the plantings. This led to escalating passive-aggressive insinuations about who was breaking the rules, and when that got us nowhere, to the reconciliatory writing of an angry letter to the neighbor (not Betti, who's allergic) about her failure to contain her nauseous cat. Thank God Manuel stopped us before we slipped the letter under her door. "It's alive," he told us, and sure enough, there it was on the Internet, even yellower than ours, with a name that was gross, funny, sublimely exact: *Dog Vomit Slime Mold.* Truly! It pops up overnight, like magic, spreading spore and discord. But now with the drought we don't see it anymore.

Betti returns, carrying two steaming cups, and drags over another chair. "Salud," she says. She taps her mug to mine. "Don't get excited.

I'm way too old. I'm just keeping you company."

It feels strange to be drinking something hot that doesn't have any flavor. I wonder if I should offer some to Manuel. I always propose sodas or lemonade or filtered ice water, and he almost always refuses. He says he keeps a cooler in his truck.

Betti's talking earnestly again about her show. "*The Caregiver.* Too heavy, right? And I kind of liked *The Giver,* but then my manager told me that's the name of a book the kids all have to read in school."

"*The Sitter?*" I ask.

"I like that, I thought of that too. My manager says it sounds like a horror movie franchise. Then I had a dream and the name *Sitter City* came to me in the dream and I figured that was a sign, that was it, but after a day of loving this name, I ultimately realized that it sounds like there are *lots* of sitters on the show, an entire city of sitters, when in fact it's only me. *I'm* the sitter."

"*Sitter in the City—*"

"And that was my major breakthrough: Me! Why not embrace it? There's a great tradition."

She takes a long, careful sip of her water and looks at me expectantly over the rim of her cup.

I hesitate. "You want to call the show *Betti?*"

She stomps her right foot, and her pointy heel sinks into the space between the pavers. "How did you know!"

For a moment it's unclear whether she's angry or delighted.

"It works, right?" She bends down and extracts her shoe. "It was staring us in the face the whole time. I mean, think about it: *Alice, Maude, Rhoda, Phyllis...*"

"*Betti,*" I say. "It's easy to remember."

"Right? Pretty catchy. I'm so fucking relieved. I mean, it's the name of my character, Betti Escobedo," she clarifies, modestly, "and even though it's an ensemble cast, she's the heart of the show."

"*Betti,*" I repeat, and she lets out a sigh.

I look over: she isn't kidding. She is genuinely relieved. She is in fact awash in relief: eyes closed, head dropped back in her chair, face turned to the sun. All it took was a name? A meeting with Amy and a name? This is the closest I've ever come to seeing Betti in a state of rest. You could even say she looks at peace, though not in a dead way.

But the relief does do something strange to Betti's face. For the first time, I see a trace of looseness there. Tipped back, at rest, it reminds me of what a circus tent might look like from a distance in the split second after the tent poles have been pulled down by the carnies. The tent hasn't started to sink yet, but you can see that it's just about to. That last moment of tension before everything gently ripples, then gives way. Now this is a ridiculous comparison for me to make, because I've never in my life seen such a thing occur, and I don't even know if they dismantle the tent poles first, or if carnies are the ones to do it, or if that's even the correct word for people who work behind the scenes at a circus. But it seems easier to imagine a sight I've never seen before than it is to notice the slight heaviness under her jaw, or how her foundation lies dustily on top of her skin. Pouching. Crepey. Horrible words! Criminal to even think them in a sentence.

I sip my hot water and try to visualize my warm, humid interiors. I can't tell if this is an inane or a marvelous thing to be doing. I guess, like Betti's face, that its integrity depends on the angle you see it from. Because in some lights my life appears grotesque to me. Here I am sitting in the sun, holding a mug and having a chat as if there isn't a man on his hands and knees just a few yards away from me, being paid to do something I could very well do myself, something I could be doing instead of half-listening to the career plans of an aging character actress as we both gaze absently at the manic, aimless behavior of my traumatized rescue dog. What a ludicrous scene! So absurd and rotten. So disgusting that it makes me want to throw up—yes—right there on the mulch.

But the thought of Dog Vomit Slime Mold cheers me up a bit. As Manuel said, it's alive. It's part of a much bigger system, all of it growing and decomposing and feeding off itself. And sometimes, if I tilt my thinking a little to one side, I feel as if I live a magical life and am part of a huge and beautiful system. I think about the chickens I'm going to raise, and the healthy child I'm going to have one day. I think about the people at night in their headlamps and how I'm supporting a struggling economy just by putting out my recycling every week. I think what a blessing it is to be drinking hot water with Betti Pérez, who seems as wonderful to me now as she did twenty-five years ago, when she was operating the hand-crank elevator at Danceteria.

One of Amy's favorite phrases to say to me is, "Don't overthink it." She says it when I get flustered and worked up over something.

She said it when we were deciding to buy this house, and when we redid the landscaping, and again when we were standing on the sidewalk, looking at Hank huddled inside a plastic crate. And in most cases, she's been right. The dog, for instance. He's crazy and inscrutable, but he loves us unreservedly. When he's not acting in an alarming way, he's a great comfort to be around. It can make me happy simply to watch him, like it does now. He lopes easily back and forth across the yard— once, twice, three times, ignoring Manuel all the while, then finding a spot that he likes near the fence, he settles back on his haunches, collapses onto his side, stretches out his front legs, and lays his head down on the grass. My good boy.

"Guess what." Betti's eyes open; her head pops up. "My little man came back! And this time he actually smiled at me."

All of her old indignation has turned into high spirits. Again, Amy? What an effect. But now I am the one who feels relieved: Betti's face has come back into focus.

"And you know what? He has a humongous gap between his front teeth. You could drive a truck through there."

"I thought Manuel—"

At the sound of his name, Manuel glances over at us, alert.

"Oh, he did. He did. The gate's working again. It's fine." Betti waves at him. "Thank you, Manuel!" She says his name not like I do but with a good accent, the *a* sounding as if it's been flattened by the warm palm of someone's hand.

Then, without warning, they begin speaking to each other in Spanish. Energetically, as if they have a lot to express. I didn't know before now that Betti could speak Spanish, and at some points I'm uncertain if she actually can or if she's just delivering a few key words with the help of many eloquent hand gestures. I wonder if they're discussing the gate repair, because in the midst of their back-and-forth I hear my own name, but soon I think that the scope of their conversation is wider than that, because occasionally I catch Amy's name too. Listening to them talk about us but not understanding what they're saying doesn't feel as bad as you think it might; in fact it feels like pulling a blanket up to your chin and resting underneath it.

Betti says something that makes the two of them laugh. "He's being nice to me. I can barely put a sentence together." She gives Manuel another wave. "But we agree. The gate doesn't really make a difference, bunny."

Her chair scrapes against the pavers as she scoots closer. "According to him, a gate doesn't do shit!" she says gaily. "I get it. The little man's just trying to handle his business. Just doing what he's got to do." She leans across and pokes me in the arm. "I bet he likes eggs."

She winks at me. Now she looks perfectly herself again: immaculate, ironclad, ready for anything.

Back by the fence, Hank starts digging furiously.

NICK DYBEK

Three Summers

The spring I turned ten my father told me we'd be spending a month
in Maine with old friends.

"They have a daughter who's a little older than you, Josh. And it's
time I taught you to fish," he said. "You remember the Izelins, don't
you?"

I didn't, not exactly. They'd stayed with us for a night when I was
three or four. I remembered a silver Chevette with a New York license
plate at the end of our driveway, a pair of giant, torn sneakers by the
door. That was it. Roy was a professor of ornithology at the University
of Buffalo. Jan was a pharmacist. But I knew them only as voices on the
phone and as players in my parents' stories, stories that usually began,
"Once, before you were born..."

Before I was born my father had served in the Peace Corps with
Roy in Indonesia, and a few years later they overlapped at Duke. By
the time I dropped into the world, my parents had jobs at a college in
Priscilla, Nebraska. My mother was a musicologist, and at nine I could
identify most of the piano works of Erik Satie by ear. My father was a
James Agee scholar, and so devoted to the man that he often read aloud
from *Let Us Now Praise Famous Men* before dinner.

We lived on the literal edge of town. Behind our house there was
nothing but fields, and fields, and fields. Exile was the word my mother
used to describe it. But it wasn't exile to me. It was all I knew. I knew
the evenings my father and I played catch in the soft grass behind our
house. I knew that as the sun went down I'd look up to see his arm
stretching into the twilight, the ball vanishing in the darkness and
reappearing above my glove. I knew that we would continue until,
across the field in the half dark, my father looked like a shadow and
I could only listen for the pop of ball to glove. The summer I met the
Izelins my parents had just begun to take the faint shapes of people.

Roy Izelin stood on the front porch of the summerhouse. As we pulled
into the driveway in the convertible my father had rented at the airport,
Roy gestured at the house with both arms, as if conducting an orchestra.

My father bounded out of the car. Roy kissed my mother on the mouth. The air was cool and thin.

"I remember this guy," Roy said, looking down at me through green-tinted glasses. "You remember me?"

I shook my head and Roy mimicked. His ponytail followed, as if it were a snake he'd charmed. "Jacko," he said. "Look at this place, will you? I'm almost too excited." Roy grabbed a handful of his pants at the groin and shook it at my father. My father grabbed the crotch of his own pants, laughing, and my mother began to laugh too.

"Goddamn, it is. Man oh man, Roy, where did you find this fucking place?"

The house made an impression, I had to admit: the paint the color of a storm, the second-story windows gabled like heavy-lidded eyes, the bracketing under the porch like crooked teeth.

"Do some exploring. This is your vacation too," my mother said. I'd hauled her suitcase onto the porch, and as she bent to lift it the sun shone through the curtain of her hair.

There was a girl in the backyard with a book in her lap and two horse-shaped barrettes in her hair. She wore a western shirt belted at the waist like a dress.

"I'm Carol," she said, without looking up. "But don't tell me who you are."

"Why not?"

"You could be the Jordans' kid," she said. "But you could be anybody. You could be William Kidd. You could be William H. Bonney."

"Who?"

"They're outlaws. Killers."

"I've never killed anyone."

"That's what you say," Carol said, letting the book slide from her lap as she got to her feet. Her ankles were caked in mud. Her eyes were green. "That's what Captain Kidd said too, but when it was time to bury his treasure, he'd anchor his pirate ship and row to shore on a boat with one of his men. He'd have that poor sucker help him dig a hole, and then he'd cut his throat right there."

"Obviously," I said. "So only he'd know where the treasure was."

"Follow me," she said. She took the back steps in two leaping strides and slipped into the house, emerging a moment later with an empty coffee mug. She ran into the woods behind the house and I followed. Leaves and twigs rustled and snapped under her feet; it sounded as if the ground were on fire.

The woods ended abruptly at a ledge before the line of high tide. The beach below was littered with bouquets of seaweed. Black rocks crusted with barnacles jutted from the mud. Carol slipped off her sandals and walked to the water, bare feet pressing little stamps. She dipped the cup in the surf and held it out to me with both hands.

"Don't be afraid," she said.

"I'm not drinking that," I said.

"Good idea." She nodded as if I'd finally done something smart. "Saltwater will drive you crazy. In the old days, sailors, especially pirates, used to get so thirsty that sometimes they'd forget that." She grabbed a handful of hair on either side of her face and let her feet sink into the mud. She opened her mouth and eyes wide. "They hallucinated," she said. "And do you know what they always saw? Millions of bats. With leathery wings and little red eyes, and little bat claws. They thought they were drowning in bats."

"They all saw the same thing?" I asked.

"Maybe not always. You tell me. I'll pretend I see it too."

When I didn't answer, Carol pulled her feet from the mud and began to pick her way over the rocks toward the ledge. The thought of returning to the house alone, of unpacking my bag and lying down in a new bed made my chest tight.

"What about a giant squid," I said.

Carol glanced back over her shoulder.

"Is that what the sailors saw?"

"It could be," she said.

"A giant squid with a hundred tentacles and a hundred eyes on each?" It just came out like that. I didn't recognize what I was saying. "Did you see the car we drove up in? We could pretend it's a ship."

Carol turned and took a step back toward the water. She tapped one finger on her chin. "All right," she said. "But I'm captain."

That entire afternoon we fought the squid. It attacked suddenly, tentacles sending up great jets of spray. The deck pitched and we tumbled across. I could see our reflections—soaking wet and exhausted, yet brave—in each of its hundred eyes. The hull buckled, the engine quit fighting, but we didn't, and, at last, the squid reared its flame-shaped head from beneath the waves. Its true eye was the size of the boat, and blue as the water. Carol hurled a harpoon, a desperate and perfect shot. Jets of black ink blasted across the deck as the squid howled an almost human cry of pain, then sank, fatally wounded, one tentacle slithering down the bow.

In the month that the six of us shared that house, my father took me fishing once. We sat side by side, our feet dangling from the edge of a pier. He held the rod loosely with one hand and squeezed the bridge of his nose with the other. After an hour without a bite, he said, "We'd better head in. We'll try it again tomorrow."

When we returned to the house, Roy was in the backyard bumping a volleyball into the air, his ponytail crawling down his back. "Shhh," my father whispered. Then he ran at Roy, shouting Hai-ya, tackling him around the waist, heaving until they fell to the ground, laughing.

They laughed that whole summer. Constant laughter like a sticky film on the endless stories the four of them told about four other people also named Roy, Jan, Jack, and Sarah. Jan driving my mother to the hospital in the middle of the night because she'd fallen on her face trying to walk the length of the porch on her hands, a cigarette in her mouth. A good mutual friend who'd kidnapped his own son because he was certain his ex-wife was brainwashing him, who'd showed up in Durham, looking to trade mescaline for a place to hide. Roy and my father driving through pouring rain to a farmhouse famous for the best marijuana in North Carolina, grown by a farmer willing to trade weed for books by Anaïs Nin. The road flooded and they stumbled the final mile over muddy fields, passing a bottle and shouting the lyrics to "Desolation Row" to keep warm.

"And after all that," my father said, "that farmer hands us a bag of hay. Hay! I could have fucking killed him."

"You should have fucking killed him," my mother said.

At night, they steamed clams and mussels, and the unfamiliar smells wafted through the big rooms. They drank beer as they cooked and wine during dinner, and after dinner Jan would fetch a cocktail shaker that rattled deep into night. Roy's high-pitched voice whirred like a dentist's drill. My mother swore. My father *sang*. I remember very little about Jan Izelin except that a nervous laugh followed everything she said like walky-talky static. I'd lie in bed and wait for the crescendo from the living room, the voices, the laughter, the music on the stereo. Louder and louder, until goodnights were said and doors banged shut and suddenly it was quiet enough again to hear the rumble of waves on the beach.

In the mornings, despite their swollen eyes, my mother still sliced half a banana for my cereal; my father still slid the newspaper to me across the breakfast table. But there was something different about the way they spoke. A tone of voice I recognized from when students called our house in Priscilla—impatient, dismissive.

"Look at it out there," my father said one morning. "There's some serious freedom out there. Why don't you go find it?"

Was that why I spent every moment I could with Carol? Together, we became navigators of the South Pacific. Horse trainers in Wyoming. Scientists on the moon. It was up to me to decide the game, and as the days wore on I got better at it. I had to, because any time I asked Carol what her school was like, her town, her friends, she'd flatten me with a bored expression and refuse to answer, as if guarding her real life. And any time I said, "Why don't you pick the game," she only shrugged, as if she were guarding her imagination too.

Luckily my imagination had a lot to work with. The downstairs of the house—the dining room, the kitchen, the bedrooms where my parents and the Izelins slept—was well kept, but the upstairs was shabby and neglected. To me, the peeling wallpaper and splintering floorboards were mysterious and new. The opposite of the off-white drywall of our ranch home in Priscilla, of our neighborhood with its carpets of bright sod. We ran through those hallways and threw open the doors. One door was locked.

"There must be a key," Carol said. She pressed her ear to the wood. She peered into the keyhole. "I can't tell. Can you see anything?"

I nudged her over with my shoulder, blinked into the keyhole and shook my head.

We raced down the rest of the hall, darting in and out of the rooms. Some rooms were empty, some decorated like shrines to old lives. Twin beds strapped down by moth-eaten orange blankets. Two swords crossed above a doorway. A series of posters advertising The Grand Dubrovnik Hotel. Framed maps of coastlines, intricate as treetops. An old-fashioned scale like I'd seen at the doctor's office. We were archaeologists sifting through the ruins, trying to piece together a lost civilization.

"This was a pirate's house," Carol said. "It must have been."

And one afternoon, when we pulled the clothes out of a battered dresser, hat by hat, mitten by mitten, we found a map hidden in the bottom drawer beneath a tattered black cardigan.

"Hold one side, put your knees on it," Carol said. Together, we spread the scroll across the floor. The paper was bright blue and penciled with geometric shapes.

"It's this house," Carol pronounced after a moment. "The blueprints."

There was the front door, the front hall leading into the living room, behind the living room the kitchen, off the kitchen the first floor bathroom, the distance from one room to the next spanned by squares of a faint grid. Seeing the mathematics behind it only seemed to further the mystery of the place.

"This is us." Carol pointed. "Right? But what about this?"

She pointed to another room. In the center of the square was a smaller square. Carol traced it with one finger.

"It must be the locked room. And that, my friend, is a treasure chest if I've ever seen one. Doesn't that look like a treasure chest to you?"

At dinner, while our parents sat at the table, we sat beneath it, hiding out. We heard the rap and rattle of plates and bottles. Someone overturned an ashtray and gray snow fell from the table's edge. I'd learned to stop paying attention, to let myself believe they were playing games not so different from ours. But it didn't always work. That night my father said, "You're right, Roy. You're completely fucking right. What *did* happen?" He was drunk—I could tell the signs by then— his words coming at half speed and double volume. It must be true, he said. Somewhere along the way, and he didn't know where, that was the hard part, but somewhere, he'd screwed up big. He must have, he said, if it had led him to a second-rate school that treated him to a windowless office in a building surrounded by a grid of asphalt, grass, parking lot, field. If it had led him to Priscilla, to neighbors he both pitied and resented and a basement that flooded and smelled like a body. This was all wrong.

Someone was swirling a drink, the ice chiming.

"Well," Roy said. "Serves you right for dedicating your life to James Fucking Agee. Anyone could have told you that."

"*That* was a guy who could drink," my father said.

"He could. But if you were going to slave over a drunk, why not me?" As if on command the adults laughed. I strayed too close to Roy's foot. He bent under the table and yanked me up into the light. "Here, here, look at these stowaways." He drum-rolled the table with his palms.

"What have these stowaways been up to?"

"Pirating," Carol said.

"Bravo to that." Roy began to clap and the rest of the adults joined in. "Élan, that takes some true élan. What are your pirating plans? Treasure, death, what?"

"Still deciding," Carol said.

"It's just you don't look so piratey," Roy said. "What about an eye patch, a parrot, some venereals, at least?"

"We've got a map," she said.

Roy led another round of applause. "A map. We've got to see it."

I knew Carol kept it folded in her back pocket. I'd already dreamt up a story for the map, and I could feel Roy's questions wiping away the trap doors and moss-covered tombs.

"Actually, it's a secret map," I said.

"We don't have secrets," Roy said. "Not between us. Let's see."

Carol handed Roy the map. He swept the plates in front of him aside and unfolded it across the dinner table. He made a show of studying it carefully. "Hmm, yes, I see, yes, interesting," he said.

I watched Carol watching him. Smiling. "Well?" she said.

"Come here, and I'll show you," Roy said. "You see this room here, and there's this square, here. I bet that's your treasure."

Carol rolled her eyes. "We know *that* already."

This brought the adults to hysterics.

"OK, OK," Roy said. "I figured you did, but look at the size of that square. You know, when I was living in Scotland as a kid, I went to stay with an uncle one summer, and he had a room like that. There was a chest in that room so big that it could never fit through the door. It was built in the room, built to never leave. That might be what we're dealing with here."

"What was in it?" Carol asked.

"That's a secret."

"You just said there were no secrets."

"You have an uncle in Scotland?" my mother said, giggling.

"Well, I *might*," Roy said, and in the laughter that followed I snatched the map from the table and dragged Carol away.

We returned to the house the next summer. My father rented another convertible and once we'd parked in the gravel drive I leapt out. I found Carol at the edge of the water, digging up the shore. Her arms were sleeved in mud. There was no wind to soften the smell of brine and seaweed.

"I'm glad you finally got here," she said. "You can help me."

"Help you play in the mud?"

"I'm looking. I've been thinking about this all year, about what you and I should do."

If said by the right person, no words are more powerful than "you and I."

"We should find that key," she said, using a filthy finger to push hair over one of her ears. "So we can get into that room. So we can see what's in that chest."

"You think the key's out here?" I asked.

"Maybe," Carol said, without looking up. "Are you going to help me or not?"

We'd all left the last summer, hugging and throwing bags into the convertible and saying how we'd return the next year and do it all again, and I'd stayed up nights that winter sketching out new planets. I'd dreamt of racing lava as I'd waded through knee-high Nebraska snow. I'd fled across the prairie, an Indian chased by cowboys.

I was young enough to think that it was possible for things to be exactly the same, but my parents should have known better.

"Why didn't you tell us you were coming alone?" my mother asked Roy that evening. She stood at the kitchen sink, filling the slate-colored steamer pot. Roy was bent over a cutting board, the knife clicking fast as a sewing machine.

"I didn't come alone," he said. "In fact, I brought an entire case of northern Rhône, and Carol's somewhere too."

"Why didn't you tell us *Jan* wasn't coming?" my father asked.

"I don't know. I should have." Roy ran his finger along the broad side of the knife, wiping garlic off the blade. "But the better question is why didn't she tell me she was leaving?"

My parents shared glances and a few shards of conversation about how maybe this wasn't a good idea anymore. But there was something irresistible about Roy, maybe even more so after he lost Jan. Sometimes self-destruction looks just like self-confidence, and Roy seemed invulnerable.

In fact, with Jan gone, my parents and Roy receded further into the distance. They stayed up deep into the night and slept off most of the days. In the mornings, I'd come downstairs to find the house deserted; the dining-room table littered with bottles; the ashtrays overflowing and the air stuffed with smoke.

The late nights that, the first year, had been so confusing began to seem almost funny. My father, his glasses dirty, his hair gray at the temples, lolling his head from side to side, raising a glass of Canadian Club in a toast "to the cocksuckers of Bali." My mother, wearing the ancient cardigan we'd nicknamed the Brandenburger, laughing so hard that she poured an entire glass of wine into her lap.

Then one night we were joined by a woman with deeply tanned skin and a smoky voice. She wore her dark hair pulled back and there was a mole or sore at the corner of her mouth that she'd tried to cover with lipstick. "I'm Margaret, Roy's friend," she said. "Which one of you is Carol?" We just looked at her. "I'm only joking," she said. "You're very beautiful, Carol."

Carol glared at Roy through dinner, but his attention was on Margaret. He twirled his fork and served the spaghetti. He twisted the wine bottle up in his napkin like a waiter when he refilled her glass.

Later, when Carol and I were playing Scrabble in my bedroom, music began to blare from the living room. We crept to the top of the stairs, and from there we could see the four of them dancing. My mother's head on my father's shoulder. Roy and Margaret, swaying, his hands clasped at the small of her back. His eyes closed and jaw clenched, as if it took a great force to will them shut.

"Why don't we camp out in one of the empty rooms tonight?" I asked. "There's a ton of extra pillows and blankets." The ballad ended. Before he let go, Roy lowered his lips to Margaret's brown shoulder.

Later that night, I turned out the light and lay down in the darkness. There was a ridge of shadow maybe half a foot away. There was the sigh and faint heat of Carol's breath.

"If anything goes wrong in the night just wake me up," I said. "If the pirates who lived here come back or something." I'd meant it as a joke, a jab at the year before.

"The pirates are downstairs already, don't you hear them?" she said.

"Where's your mom?" I asked.

"In New Jersey with Clark. He helps run a plastic cup company. What kind of person would want to do that? Anyway, she moved to New Jersey with him months ago."

"You stayed with your dad?"

"I had school. That's what I told her. But is it so crazy that I wanted to stay with him? Is she going to argue with me about that?"

"She shouldn't."

"Or maybe she should. I don't know. My dad's always saying he's sorry, he's sorry. I found him asleep in the car one morning. One night the police dropped him off."

"What will you do?"

"I'll probably have to move to Clark's in the fall. But I wanted to come here for the summer. I had to really beg for that."

"Really?"

"Well," she said. "I want to see what's in that chest before I die."

"What do you think is in it?" I asked.

"It could be anything. It could be a whale."

"A whale would be too big."

"A baby whale, or whale bones."

"Do you really believe that?"

"You're ruining it, Josh," she said. "Stop ruining it, OK?"

For the rest of the summer we searched for the key. We hunted through the shed out back, peering between the rusty spokes of old bicycles. We crawled into the shade under the front porch and found nothing but the gray skeletons of birds and one bright blue feather, which I saved. We emptied out the closets and rooted in the pockets of heavy winter jackets. We pawed through the paste of old leaves in the gutters.

Back in Priscilla that fall, my parents barely mentioned the Izelins. Sometimes the phone would ring late and I'd hear my father clomp down the stairs and answer (not in the voice from Maine but in his real voice). "No, Roy. I wasn't asleep yet. What's on your mind? Just slow down. We can talk, I've got time."

One night, as my parents were cooking dinner, my father said, "He wants the three of us to buy that place. Can you imagine that?"

"My god, what did you say?"

"Well, I couldn't just tell him he was crazy, could I? I wonder if we should even go back at all."

It was a question my parents discussed often that year. One evening in February my mother said, "You won't believe who called today— *Jan*, saying that Carol told her we were going back, saying she just wanted to make sure before she says yes."

My father raised his eyebrows and said nothing. Roy continued to call and my parents continued to debate, and finally they turned to me and asked, "Do *you* want to go back to Maine next summer?"

I'd turned twelve that year. I'd joined the basketball team. I'd learned how to play "Lithium" by Nirvana on the guitar, and I'd already had my first kiss with a girl who played clarinet in the school orchestra.

Carol was on the front porch when we arrived. Her hair was cut short. She wore pleated khaki shorts and sunglasses on top of her head. She was taller, much taller.

"Oh my god," she said, as she hugged me.

"How was your year?" I asked.

"It's good to see you."

As my parents lugged in their bags, I sat down on the porch next to her.

"What do you want to do?" I asked.

"I have homework," she said. "That's how stupid this new school is. Other than that it's up to you."

"You sound different," I said.

"That must be New Jersey. I don't notice the accent anymore. I wish I did but I don't."

As always, I didn't know what to make of Carol, but Roy was worse than expected. His belly looked bigger, his neck fleshier, but his legs— poking out of boxer shorts as he sleepily ground coffee—seemed too thin to support his body.

And almost immediately I could see why my parents had been hesitant to come. In Nebraska my father could shake his head at Roy, pity him, laugh at him. But in Maine my father was powerless, roaring drunk by the end of dinner. As my mother cleared the table,

Roy yelled, "Polish Fire Drill," and he and my father took off, tearing through the house, laughing furiously. They discovered the rooms upstairs, just as Carol and I had two years before. One night, they tossed the doctor's scale out of the second-story window, and it lay on the lawn for days, a mess of weights and pulleys. It was Carol who cleaned it up, Carol who helped Roy into bed that night and the next night. Pouring him a glass of water, rattling aspirin from a bottle on the bedside table.

When she wasn't taking care of Roy, Carol spent her time just as she'd promised, reading *Jane Eyre*, *Wuthering Heights*, and *Lord of the Flies*. The sun boiled away the days. By dusk, there was nothing left but heat, and the air felt thick as seawater. At night I would follow her on long walks through the woods.

These journeys turned into dares. How far could we go into the forest? Until the waves no longer sounded and the insects seemed to rise up. It was frightening, all that blackness and buzz. I could hear Carol's steps get fast and her breathing shallow, but I was always the one to suggest turning back. I was happy to, because only then— when it was just the two of us picking our way toward the glowing windows—did I feel I could talk to her.

"You know, I almost called you last fall, in November," she said one night. "Would that have been strange?"

"Did something happen?" I asked.

"Not really. Someone kicked in Clark's basement windows. I cut my foot on the broken glass. My mother thought I did it on purpose. Then we both cried for hours."

"How did you get her to let you come back?"

"That was easy. I told her this is the only place I don't think about dying all the time."

Our footsteps crunched in the dark.

"I just told her that," Carol said. "I don't really think about dying all the time."

"What do you think about?" I asked.

"My mother says I need to stop pretending that nothing's changed, because everything has, and that's life. She says some people never stop believing in the past. Do you think I've changed? Since you've known me?"

"I'd say yes."

"I knew you did. I can always see it on your face when you get here. It's nice actually."

"Have I changed?"

She laughed. "No," she said. "Not really. Don't worry, though. There's time."

But there wasn't. A few nights later I was awoken by shouts from the yard. The air was doused with fog, but from my window I could pick out the shapes of Roy and my father. Each held a sword pulled from the wall upstairs. The enormous moon seemed to be held in place by a string of cloud.

"Avast, lover," I heard my father say.

"You mean lubber," Roy said. "Prepare for a keel haul under me big balls."

They rushed at each other. The swords gleamed and clinked as they passed like jousters. My father stumbled a few steps and sat down, laughing hysterically. I heard the back door open and crack shut. "OK, enough of that," my mother said. "I wasn't serious about a duel."

But Roy and my father ignored her and began the dance again, rushing, shouting. This time my father dropped his sword and went down, howling. My mother ran out and reached for his bleeding hand.

"What the hell is wrong with you?" she said.

"He's a scurvy dog. That's what's wrong with him," Roy said.

By the time I got downstairs there was a trail of blood through the kitchen, yards of paper towel and the beginning of a debate about the emergency room. My father stood, bleeding into the sink, looking more sober, more embarrassed than I'd ever seen him.

He wore the same expression the next afternoon as my mother asked me to have a seat in the living room. She said she was sorry, but it was best for everyone if we left. It wasn't anyone's fault, she said, and it had been fun—no one was saying that it hadn't. She addressed everything to Roy because my father—holding his bandaged hand above his head—had apparently already agreed.

Roy stared at the floor, looking a million years old. They were all too embarrassed to say much else, so my mother turned to me.

"Why don't you get packed up," she said.

"I should tell Carol," I said.

"Please do," Roy said, tilting up his tired eyes. "I have to call her mother."

I didn't have to tell her. I'd seen her at the top of the stairs, listening. Just where we'd stood the summer before, watching Roy dance with that woman. I imagined Carol and me dancing. I imagined her returning home to New Jersey, her feet bleeding on a white rug in her bedroom.

I looked for the blue feather I'd taken from under the porch the year before. I dug through the dresser where we'd found the map, tied a scarf around my head, and stuck the feather behind it. I found a fedora that looked enough like a cowboy hat, tied another scarf into a holster, bent a wire hanger into a pistol.

I stood in the doorway of Carol's room. Her eyes were red. She sat with her arms around one knee. I drew back the arrow on an invisible bow.

"Come on," she said, laughing and crying at the same time. "What is this?"

"Run," I said.

She tied on the holster, drew the coat hanger and pointed it at me.

"You run," she said.

She chased me through the halls all the way back to Nebraska. I licked at the flint of an arrowhead as I waded through a cold white river, slid on my belly through tall grass, under the enormous heads of buffalo and a sky knotted with clouds. Across the prairie, I saw her silhouette, dark except for one silver glint as she pulled a key from a tangle of dry weeds.

Then we were back in the house, racing down the hall to the door. Carol's hair was long, and she wore horse-shaped barrettes. Jan was downstairs rattling a cocktail shaker, laughing with Roy and my mother and father.

The key rattled too, but the lock finally turned. As the door swung free, light poured into the dark hall. No one had been in the room for years and it was as if all the light had been saved up.

The chest inside was mammoth. Built from dark wood, it was unadorned except for a keyhole. Carol stood in front of it, arms outspread as if she might rise off the floor. The chest was wider than her wingspan. The sunlight rolled over the rounded top and struck her hair. She turned the key and heaved it open.

"It's full of water," she said.

She dove in headfirst and after a moment I followed, swimming through a shoal of black fish to the bottom of an ocean. Carol's hair streamed like flame. We exchanged messages in bubbles of air. We took giant steps along the seafloor, weaving between stingrays, kicking up showers of sand, until we found another chest crusted in barnacles. We pried the second chest open too: inside there was another shimmering pool. She took my hand and dove again through cold currents. We emerged above a reef lit up like a city. Another chest filled with water. We continued, to another chest and another. Down and down and down until, from the living room, I heard my mother calling my name.

Soon after, I was on my way to the airport, and soon after that, I was in high school. And soon after that, the friends I'd played pick-up basketball with were tuning muscle cars and I'd begun to feel angry and alone. My parents, with all of their social realist literature and Ravel, had made me an outsider in my own hometown, had left me no choice but to look at my classmates with a mixture of jealousy and contempt. When I left Priscilla, I went straight to San Francisco and stayed on after college and planned never to leave. I guess it should have been no surprise that Carol would wind up there too. It should have been no surprise to hear her voice on my machine one evening after work, but it was.

We got together at a bar in the Mission. We hadn't seen each other in over ten years, and I can't say I would have recognized her if we'd passed on the street. She was thin and sort of Nordic-looking with teeth like Liv Ullmann's. She took my hand and led me upstairs to a lounge with leather chairs where it was stifling hot and loud. She spoke fast, and had a nervous way of laughing, just like her mother. Roy, she told me, had quit drinking years ago, he'd just retired and was working on restoring a little cottage on Owasco Lake. She'd spent two years at Tufts before an anxiety attack drove her out west. She loved San Francisco. She was taking a poetry class at City Lights and learning to sail at the marina and feeling much better. She was still working on her degree and just waiting for credits to transfer and temping in the meantime as the receptionist at a bank.

"And your parents?" she asked.

"Nearly retired. I think they're happy," which I said automatically because I could still never think of them as anything other than happy. "You know," she said, "those were some bad years for me. I never really thanked you. I must have been so self-absorbed. Were they bad for you?"

"No," I said. "They weren't bad. I even miss them sometimes."

"I don't, but you know what I was thinking the other day after I called? I'll never have another friend like that. All of a sudden, it's too late."

The music went up and we had to lean close to each other's ear to be heard. I caught every third word about a therapist in Boston, about an old boyfriend. I could tell she was missing much of what I was saying, though much of what I was saying wasn't important. Eventually, she said that she had friends to meet and that I should come too, and I told her that I had friends to meet as well, even though I didn't.

Really, I was just tired. I'd taken a job teaching history at a junior high school in Oakland. Each morning, I stood in line for the metal detector behind shoving eighth graders, cleaning the change from my pockets. Each day, I came home with stacks of crumpled notebook paper to read, already so exhausted that my teeth hurt.

We promised to call, but I knew that I probably wouldn't see her again. There are only so many people you can have in your life, and three summers spent together half a lifetime before just wasn't enough. I walked home thinking this but also imagining—it just came to me, I couldn't shake the image   that I'd climb the dark stairs to my apartment and twist the sticky lock and shoulder open the heavy door to find her there, waiting.

STUART DYBEK
Misterioso

"You're going to leave your watch on?"
"You're leaving on your cross?"

CAROLYN FERRELL

Before They Were Flesh-Eating Zombies Trying to Take Over the World

Winston Hall-Miles

Worked as Head Janitor at Tungsten Middle and High Schools and had been, by most accounts, satisfied with the way life treated him. Never any trouble with the law, never married, no kids anywhere. Took his job serious as a heart attack: kept the hallways neat, the floors in the school library polished, the couches in the teachers' lounge fresh with baking soda. Subscribed to *Popular Mechanics, Ebony, Good House-keeping;* drank malt liquor; roasted one chicken for a week's worth of meals, marrow soup being the last. When the so-called *Kafkatization of Mankind*[1] hit town in 1991, Hall-Miles was among the first to exhibit symptoms, though of course we didn't recognize them for what they were. Sulking in the supermarket, scratching at the bowling alley— we did, in fact, think he seemed somewhat different, though it took us a short minute to understand the physical reality of his situation.[2]

---

[1] *Kafkatization* is a term that has grown out of a lot of other less worthy classifications employed to describe the Change and all its manifestations. The term *zombie* is insufficient and insulting, for instance. Similarly, the term *undead* is usually used in vampyrical classifications and, like *zombie,* has proven itself insufficient. Around 1990, researchers at Brookhaven Labs came up with the term *Kafkatization,* which they went on to describe in lay terms as the "permanent undoing of human machinery that is life as we know it." Kafkatization occurs after the brain has ceased all memory functions; when it is no longer able to distinguish pleasure from pain, black from white, Nigerian from Australian, sweet from sour. Think of it as your brain on super-autopilot. All that registers is the survival instinct, maybe a few colors, smells, perhaps an occasional face, though that is extremely rare. A reanimation of the corpus takes place, a reigniting that is dark, homely, and unwieldy. We are still learning about this condition, even at this latter-day stage. What has been generally affirmed, however, is the manner in which an end comes to the Afflicted. True termination of the Kafkatized coincides with the complete severing of the spinal cord. It does not—as in classic movies like *Night of the Living Dead, Dawn of the Dead, Zombie Nightmare,* etc.—end with a bullet to the noggin.

[2] Due to his naturally reserved nature.

Hall-Miles did not walk like a stiff, nor did he have skin folding on his body in unsightly rags, nor did he once speak like Sylvester Stallone in *Rocky I* through *V*. You could say a light went out in his eyes, that something akin to bewilderment draped itself over his face. He began to smell funny. His nails were unsightly, growing like scythes at the ends of his fingers. After weeks of clandestine observation, the Brookhaven Labs researchers determined that Winston Hall-Miles did not actually eat or drink anything.[3] They noted, however, that his janitorial skills remained impeccable.

In fact, the last words he uttered before the Total Transmutation were: *Come here and clean this mess up, you no-good hoodlum!*

Those words were directed at a twelfth-grade boy (Frank White) who'd spat tobacco on Mr. Hall-Miles' newly waxed gym floor. Strange to hear a grown man talk to a boy in this way? Not really, given the poor man's arthritis and the fact that he most times cussed out the kids at Tungsten Middle and High. But as previously mentioned, his speech never got strange. He never lost words or fell victim to mumbling or garbled his meanings. Case in point: on the evening of the tobacco incident, Mr. Hall-Miles was heard (and seen) singing the "Star Spangled Banner," in a precise and lovely baritone, right outside Tungsten Union Free Library. No words slurred, swallowed, or otherwise distorted. He perched on the statue of the Union Soldier and twirled himself in the statue's arms, a discombobulated Ben Vereen. When forced by the Tungsten P.D. to come down from the statue's pedestal, he jumped, and his left arm danced off his body like a petal from a rose.[4]

After some chase, Winston Hall-Miles was euthanized in the large female-shaped hedge outside Jugglers Bar and Grille. In the morning, his home was ignited and burned to the ground; this was, of course, in the days when we thought that fire would make a difference.

And during the funeral service—because in those days we also

---

[3] Another interesting fact: those affected by Kafkatization do not prefer the taste of human brains over other bodily foodstuffs.

[4] An additional myth worth destroying is that of the slow, cumbersome zombie. After jumping and losing his arm, Winston Hall-Miles sprinted like a tenth-grade track star down Village Street. He was seen giving the remaining middle finger to Sheriff Hal Roman, who plodded after Winston in typical doughnut-infused fury.

thought that actual burials were the right way to go—we talked among ourselves and uncovered additional tidbits about this untimely victim. Call it gossip, tongue-wagging. The people from Brookhaven Labs who walked around the cemetery with legal pads and recorders thought we were quaint. They asked us to act like they weren't there. They asked us to speak clearly. They asked us to simply give them the "facts."

But can pure "facts" ever really tell the whole story? Here is what we had at first:

1) Winston Hall-Miles was in actuality not much older than the kids he swept up after.

2) His father, a retired janitor, encouraged his son to consider university as the true path in life. He stopped speaking to Winston five years before his death.

3) His mother signed her name with an X. She often appeared in Winston's dreams at night, wearing Cuban heels, her face hidden in shadow.

4) Winston Hall-Miles could not stand chicken.

Stories like these did indeed help us start to make sense of things, but in the end, what sense did *anything* make to *anyone?* Times grew bad, almost overnight. No one could look you in the eye and say with certainty: *I get it.* Even at Brookhaven Labs, there was the occasional lull in understanding, big empty spaces where there should have been answers. A question mark smack in the middle of everyone's face.

One year later, after compiling facts for Winston's Memorial, additional "facts" revealed themselves:

5) A distant father does not necessarily mean you will one day pit yourself against humanity.

6) Idle hands are the work of the devil.

Shawntelle Fountain

Ran an underground, unlicensed, and unauthorized day care out of her home. You remember the place—smelled like a toilet from three houses in either direction. Shawntelle herself had three kids from that Black Panther boyfriend—it was said she turned down a scholarship to Columbia University in order to be with him.

Going nowhere fast, people said.

Some years later, Shawntelle did, in fact, leave this boyfriend and all his pamphlets and Afro picks. People said that she fell in love with a white boy from Pomegranate Township—fell so much in love that her head practically took itself off into the clouds.

A white boy! You know how people can talk.

More time passed. In June of 1998 a letter appeared in the *Columbia Daily Specter* with the following headline: "WHITE DEVIL FEVER HITS BLACK POPULATION LIKE THE PLAGUE!!!"

This of course being attributed to Shawntelle's baby daddy. Supposedly, he was served a cease and desist letter from Columbia University, as well as the Suffolk County chapter of Parents Without Partners. Who knows for sure?

After her Change,[5] Shawntelle's three kids were placed with her sister, Mary Fountain, who was quoted in the *Columbia Daily Specter* as saying, "I always knew that what goes around comes around. That white boy couldn't dance, smelled like soap, and wouldn't know a good chicken wing if it beat him in the face."

Hush that, we told Mary Fountain.

To no avail; jealousy being another of those traits that did not disappear with the *Kafkatization of Mankind as We Know It*.

Mrs. Georgia Fields

Could not, as a longtime church mother at the Tungsten Faith A.M.E., understand why God had made her sons so damn prolific. Handsome, every last one of them. But prolific like you would not believe. As if they'd been born with something otherworldly in their eyes.

When he was in the eleventh grade, her eldest, Paul, came home crying about some girl. October 29, 1991—he kissed the top of his mother's head and asked politely if he could have some money.

Polite being the operative word. *Kissed*, as well.

How come, asked Georgia. They sat at the kitchen table in front of a pan of biscuits. Eyelet curtains blew in the early evening breeze.

There's a place in Lindenhurst, Paul said. They say the girl is in and out like nothing ever happened.

How come, Georgia repeated.

---

[5]Nothing happened at all to the white boy. He is still living in Tungsten, healthy as a fish, with all of Shawntelle's photographs upon the wall.

Paul said he didn't want this bitch ruining his life forever.

Georgia—we always knew her as pious, wooden, ungentrified—felt her mind implode. She'd always been grateful to be a mother of future men. What would God say, though, if He knew what her son was planning? God's sacred laws were many, the first one being: Ignorance is the mother of devotion.[6]

God would never, however, turn a blind eye to a "procedure." The kitchen TV blared the six o'clock news: more war somewhere where they manufactured gas for cars and RVs. No, a procedure was out of the question. She would not hear of anything having to do with suction, vacuums, cotton gauze, sympathetic receptionists, dim lights, or protest marches. Georgia looked at her son with warm eyes. I always wanted me a little girl, she mumbled. Make her plaits. Take her camping out near Montauk. Remember how we went that time in the RV?

(God's Sacred Law No. 2: Everything you can imagine is real.[7])

But a year later, in the twelfth grade, it was Paul again, bothered by some new skank claiming to have a so-called "bun in the oven." When he came to his mother this time, he wanted money to take the girl to Mexico. We'll borrow your RV and be back in two weeks, he insisted. Mexico is just round the corner from Raleigh and you remember how long it took to get there when I was ten and we had Grandma's reunion? A little more than ten hours, and I swear I won't mess the RV up. Remember all that fun at Grandma's reunion, *all that pork barbecue?*

Paul added, We thinking about getting married, so why not have the honeymoon before the brat gets here?

Georgia closed her eyes right there in front of *Family Feud*[8] and prayed and prayed. She had five sons.

Paul wound up having just the two, no wedding ever in sight. Sons Peter and Mark had one apiece, both in the tenth grade. Simon was different in that he got his start in the ninth grade—what some at the Tungsten Faith A.M.E. found to be a possible baby-daddy world record until the youngest son Quaysan knocked up a girl in the eighth grade. That was low, Georgia said to herself. Eighth grade.

---

[6] Attributed to Robert Burton, English clergyman, 1577-1640.

[7] Attributed to Pablo Picasso, artist, 1881-1973.

[8] No pun intended.

Could it get any lower?

She supplicated. God's Sacred Law No. 3: Ask and Ye Shall Receive.[9] Quaysan had subsequent girl trouble in ninth, tenth, and twelfth grades. Rumors spread about him, that he was a user, a demon, a monster. Georgia turned the other cheek. But just as her baby boy was about to graduate high school, Georgia got down on her knees, something she hadn't been able to accomplish in years. God had to look down and lead this one, *her last baby*.

Nothing seemed to halt Quaysan's proliferation nor deter the loving feelings blooming in any of the females. He'd brought them all home— Keisha, Tijuana, Michelline, Margaret—and gave them free reign of his mother's perfectly slipcovered house. Television, pound cake, lemon wax, and Downy sheets. He was no more than seventeen at his most high volume.[10]

Then one day just after graduation, Georgia asked Quaysan to come and watch the last minutes of *Search for Tomorrow* with her (stories, of course, being her favorite release). He'd just returned from hanging out at the old handball court and wishing he was still in the twelfth; around him, summer leaves shivered from the maples and birds flew in circles over the chimneys. His mother, always a pretty picture, patted a place on the slipcovered couch; when he sat, she laughed.

In all the years he was on this earth, Quaysan had never heard his mother laugh.

And now, with the late afternoon sun turning the walls of the living room all shades of crimson and goose down, Quaysan noticed that his mom was looking at him funny. He noticed the way her hands shook. She spoke in a soprano—unusual, since most people thought she

---

[9]Sacred Law No. 3 Addendum: Be Specific in Your Request. God Is Not No Mind Reader. Attributed to Georgia Fields, beleaguered mother, 1947-1997.

[10]Curiously, romance has been discovered by Brookhaven researchers to unleash a certain chemical preservative in the physiology of the so-called roaming dead. It had long been assumed that the Kafkatized had no other desire but to walk the earth, eat living humans, and scare the hell out of innocent bystanders. Quaysan Fields proved that love offered some swagger against decrepitude. Though he exhibited signs of the very essence of Descent—the blackened fingertips and toes, the afro chock full of dust mites and spider eggs, the lungs producing their own equivalent of natural formaldehyde— Quaysan Fields kept on trying to rap to Daphine Hammond—Head Cheerleader at Tungsten High—right up until the very end.

normally sounded a lot like Sylvester Stallone. *You ain't think one minute about being tested, have you?* she asked. *Why are you such a bastard?*

Quaysan felt a numbing thunder go through his feet. His mother was not in the habit of asking questions.

That night he heard her praying at her bedside: *Lord, Why Dost Thou Forsake Me? And though worms devour this Monster Mash, why dost Thou... Amen and Forevermore.*

These words were said to have deeply affected Quaysan, though he couldn't pinpoint why. He would not have time to unravel the mystery: five days later, while serving dinner (pork chops and applesauce), his mother leaned over the table and took a bite out of his hand.

You can imagine the mayhem.

Georgia Fields ran into the street braving the cold with only a dress and apron on—no stockings. Her body fell apart conveniently outside the gates of Tungsten Cemetery.

Quaysan disappeared after her into the street; metamorphosing hours later behind the hospital buildings on Feather Lane; scaring the daylights out of a bunch of innocent marijuana-smoking high-schoolers. He was later Undone by members of the National Guard, all armed with top-notch assault rifles.

Again, in this case—as in all cases—the desire for answers brewed fervently in our breasts. What had the world turned into? Those fools at Brookhaven Labs seemed blind as bats and deaf as doorknobs. What was the cause of this zombification? And why did it happen to those who least deserved it?

At his dying moment, Quaysan saw his life flash before his eyes[11]— the last clear picture being his mother's shaking hands and her mouth in a clean-cut: *Why, why, why?* The Guard brought his body back to the labs for forensic exploration and discovery, and no word on Quaysan Fields was ever heard again.

That is, if you don't count that one time, in the knitting circle at the Tungsten Faith A.M.E, when some elderly deaconesses made the observation that when you have five sons, when would your hands *not* be shaking?

---

[11]This is something that does actually happen—ask any one of us.

Handsome and pretty the pair of them, with unusually soft hands and large cherubic smiles. Legally husband and wife, though some said they were a secret sister and brother, or else fag and dyke. Other possibilities abounded but who really cared?[12] Hung a rainbow-hued welcome flag outside their nursery. Ate organic. Remained largely childless.

Migdalia and Henry ran the Agosto-Ball Evergreen Emporium over on Douglas Boulevard, a mile from the Great South Bay. Not officially trained as botanists or horticulturalists, but knew their way around the inner life of plants better than Gregor Mendel and his pea flowers. Came up with various hybrids over the years, such as the Fractured Rose and Firebrand Forsythia; dabbled here and there in landscaping, but felt most at home in the greenhouse behind the ornamental trees, where they worked tirelessly to come up with the perfect Tungsten shrub. Never became members of the A.M.E. or the Praise Tabernacle.

Rumors about such a couple abounded until the end.

They talked about retiring to the Dominican Republic, where Migdalia still had people. Put most of their gardening goods on sale four times a year, lamented the onslaught of home improvement stores, many of which were putting them out of business. Nineteen ninety-three was a particularly bad year. Migdalia Agosto-Ball was quoted (in the produce aisle of the A&P) as saying, "Something better happen, Henry, something big."

Famous last words.

Later on, it was surmised by certain technical minds (sent down from the Naval Research Lab in Washington, D.C.) that the chemicals in the peat moss, fertilizer, and other lawn products might have something to do with the haste in which the couple Translated themselves into Automatons.

For the longest time, no one would believe in the Kafkatization of those two. In spite of the rumors—sister-brother love? Drag-queen intrigue?—they seemed perhaps the most normal of normal folks on Long Island. And yet.

One day Henry's teeth fell out in mid-sentence as he was talking about how much Weed-B-Gon to use; over by the Christmas Clearance nook,

---

[12]Tungsten tongues could best any others at wagging!

Migdalia started pulling at her hair, which came out in long, carnivorous ribbons.

In the days that followed, people didn't want to buy their plants and tools from the Agosto-Balls anymore. After two weeks, a GOING-OUT-OF-BUSINESS sign was hung off the huge evergreen in the parking lot, and that was that.

In the end, a group of Navy guys offered to do the Eradication at low cost, "just like the spaying/neutering at the Tungsten ASPCA." They said they were not into the "business aspect" of ridding Tungsten of its undead threat. They just wanted to work to restore normalcy, in any way they could. This was a small-town thing, and demanded a small-town response.

And as a token of goodwill, those sailors threw in the Post-Death Death and Cleanup for free. Just sign here, they said to Migdalia's people, who'd come up from Puerto Plata in no time flat.[13]

Chandra Gore

The joke being that her name was the "writing on the wall."

Politically, she was a turning point in the Kafkatization of Events: after she underwent the Change—this had to be late 1995—there were indeed a lot of "aha" moments. Scientists and researchers looked at her as a catalyst: Chandra was like that black woman whose cells were taken from her corpse, but then she went and started to cure cancer from the grave without knowing what the hell was going on.

People heard about Chandra and felt they could talk about what was happening with openness and clarity.[14]

---

[13]Particularly galling was the increasing insistence, by fame-seeking politicians cashing in on the tragedy, that man-made chemicals—fertilizer, weed killers—were at the heart of the Human Disaster. The Agosto-Balls were not Dr. Frankenstein. Though an inordinate amount of test tubes, Bunsen burners, and chemical compounds were found in their greenhouse, there is no evidence that they were evil geniuses. The shrub they'd been developing turned out to be nothing more than the common Rose of Sharon.

[14]Recorded testimony taken by Brookhaven researchers from random Tungsten citizens: "Matter of fact, my wife did look like death warmed over—and then I realized that that's what she *actually was!*"

"Honey, listen up. Never love a zombie. They will forget every good thing you ever done did for them." "Amen to that."

Chandra Gore was seventeen and a regular member of the Tungsten Key Club. She was a candy striper at Brunswick Hospital. She babysat for the kids on Feather Lane in her spare time. How she became infected we will never know. One day, she was changing bandages and making cups of tea for the old folks in the nursing home wing. Next thing, she was complaining about feeling weird, cold and hot at the same time. Tongue thick in her mouth like a loaf of stale bread.

All eyes were on the poor girl.

It must be stated that Chandra was the type who was not normally noticed by anyone at all. Not at school, not at the Key Club (where all the teens did was practice dance moves and smoke joints in the basement), not in the hospital (except for a few oldsters who longed for the songbird of youth). At home there were troubles. Her mother debated on whether to file charges against her brother, the one who spent at least two years asking Chandra to be "his in a special way." Two of Chandra's brothers went into the Marines during the Big War, came out covered in Agent Orange insanity. A sister was deemed to be mongoloid.

After ascertaining that Chandra was "possibly" no longer "among the living," they took her to Brookhaven and put her into quarantine, even though there were no glaring symptoms. They thought, however: better safe than sorry.[15]

She was just a plain girl in a plain town. If you'd blinked, she would've disappeared in that very space.

And then she was gone; *Extinguished;* and when we learned the news, a great sorrow flowed throughout Tungsten. A truly despondent community—though at first, we couldn't really explain it. How do you mourn someone who didn't really register in the first place?

Gradually, our sadness naturally turned into questions of a more conspiratorial-theoretical nature: was this a "race" thing? Why kill a black girl when she seemed perfectly fine? Was she in some way related to Moynihan's 1965 Report on the black family—the black woman being bane of black existence? Or was the explanation less junky? Were white people trying to control Tungsten, seeing as how it had, in recent years, become desirable beachfront real estate?

---

[15]A zombie can scream just as loud as a real person. They do not have to sound like Sylvester Stallone. We were gratified to have this fact confirmed.

Some pointed to the fact that white people were coming down with all sorts of cancers—AIDS, SARS, and so on—didn't they manufacture all those illnesses in labs and then blame it all on monkeys in Africa? Were whites poisoning the waters on Long Island? Poisoning the food? Did they have as their goal the total extermination of the black race as we know it?

One of the more philosophically insightful among us (Miss Janice over at Tungsten Sweets N Things) asked: What the fucking hell was the BLACK COMMUNITY going to do about it?

Some of the old Tungsten A.M.E. church mothers wanted to do a memorial service for Chandra, even though they'd been told over and over: the person we knew and loved was gone. Gone forever. Left the building, never to return. There was no sense, the scientists observed, in mourning a bloodsucking, horrifying, creepy voodoo girl. Our best bet would be to get on with our lives.

What lives, Miss Janice asked.

The church mothers protested on the steps of Tungsten Hall—sadly to no avail. Sheriff Hal Roman was about to organize a hunger strike at the Tungsten Jail, but changed his mind when he saw that would not be a fitting statement on law enforcement.

One day, Chandra's eldest brother woke up from his Orange State and said he had learned the truth. He'd had visions, it seemed. Something in his unawake state told him what had gone down, and now he—the faithless brother he'd always been—was going to get this one thing right.

The terrible deed, the eldest told us, had been done by one of our own: the Reverend Frank White, Sr., top banana at the Tungsten Faith A.M.E.

And we learned this vision to bear truth, with the Brookhaven Labs people, of course, being behind the dirty work. You'd be doing her a favor—in the name of the Lord, the Brookhaven Labs people had told Reverend Frank. You are a man of God. You know the difference between a soul and a pestilence. We need to study that pestilence. You'd be doing all of mankind a favor.

It was said that Reverend Frank White cried real tears, not the Sunday-Pulpit kind he was famous for.

It was said that even when she looked up at him—innocent eyes, hands folded over her heart—her face had gone back to the Cross.

Pastor Elias "Buddy Boy" White

Loving husband, devoted father, maniacal Monopoly player. Operated the first storefront church in Tungsten, The Eternally Yours Praise Tabernacle. Tried to get up an angry mob in the case of Chandra Gore, was largely unsuccessful. Told his brother that he would burn in hell for the murder of Chandra Gore; broke into Tungsten Faith A.M.E. during Tuesday Night Services and raged up and down the aisles, inciting that church mob to violence.

No one moved, however. Who among us wanted the return of lynching? And if the rope worked, would the person on the other end actually die? Or would they simply cut themselves down and go on their merry, undead way?

Sheriff Roman led Buddy Boy away that night, and next thing, we saw Buddy Boy's name on the Great Gone List published daily in the *Tungsten Times*. Shame, that.

People wondered afterward if his death was a mercy killing, instead of an outright crime? Had Buddy Boy known—maybe for months, years—that he himself was already undergoing Kafkatization? Had he preached that last sermon—the parable of the mustard seed—all the while glancing at his feet, which had begun to turn green? Had he already felt the worms destroying his body while he led the choir in "Going Up Yonder"?

When the police (sent by the FBI, we heard, on a quiet weekday night) leaned him up against the wall outside Jugglers Bar and Grille, did he know their shots would be in vain?

Velda Bennymon

Girl Scout leader for thirty years. First Black Girl Scout leader on Long Island. Took troops out to the East End for overnights, then to the heart of the Poconos for the endurance trips. The girls hated those. Velda always had a smile on her face, her favorite platitude being: "Absence makes the heart grow fonder."

Last known human gesture included an arm around Migdalia Agosto, her best girl from Tungsten High in the seventies.

Zenobia Malady

Worked for seventeen years as Assistant-to-the-Head and then thirty years as Head Librarian at Tungsten Union Free Library—shelving, ordering books, solving the card catalog, and finally computerizing everything—until 1997, when, at the tender age of seventy-six, she stumbled upon the idea of creating a film series for town residents. Surely in this awful time some fun could still be had, no? That was Miss Malady's way of thinking, thank heavens.

Tungsten's drive-in had closed in 1972; ten years later, the mall movie house shut its doors. If you wanted to see a flick, you had to travel all the way to the Multiplex in Massapequa Park or even go as far as the Wyandanch *Cineaste*. Dissatisfied, Tungsteners began wandering the streets with hands stretched before them in popcorn mode, begging for a dark hall, a large screen, and a good soundtrack. Their words were unintelligible, but what they made clear was that they didn't care what movie it was.

Main thing, we got to sit in the dark and forget our woes for two hours.

The Library seemed like a strange place to show movies. But Miss Malady was only too eager to get things in motion.[16] Admission was free. Seating was folding chairs, and they had to be at least one foot apart from each other. Bathroom visits required a key, and could be for no longer than five minutes, and had to be one person at a time.

Because this was the library, popcorn was not allowed. Miss Malady complained of a rat population that the Tungsten P.D. had successfully ignored all these years. On the up side, you could bring in coffee or soda.[17]

The first and second films in the series were *Uptown Saturday Night* and *Let's Do It Again*. Folks could not get enough of Cosby and Poitier. The perfect poster children for a living, breathing world; funny too. Some said handsome.

When Brookhaven researchers subsequently went over her documents, they expressed little surprise that she would show films

---

[16]No pun intended.

[17]Diet was preferable, given the relative flimsiness of the chairs.

of this ilk.[18] So much for reading us clearly. In 2009, a Westchester Community College student discovered that Malady's actual favorite films included *The Omega Man, Legends of the Fall,* and *L'Enfant Sauvage.* She once wrote a fan letter to Cicely Tyson, after the showing of *Roots* in its entirety. It is not known whether a response was received. Attendance at the miniseries had been woeful.

The last film shown under Miss Zenobia Malady's direction was *Menace II Society.*

She had no children. Dinner was usually taken at Daisy's 24-Hour, where a few other oldsters enjoyed the pleasantries of the Twilight Dinner.[19]

Once, high off the success of *Dirty Harry,* Zenobia Malady let slip that she really dug Clint Eastwood. Did God frown upon interracial love fantasies? She couldn't care less. When asked, at the tender age of seventy-nine, if she believed in an afterlife, Zenobia Malady made a very un-librarian-like gesture that looked like *Go ahead, make my day.*

After her death, there was some rancor. The Salvation Army refused most of her personal effects, as did Big Brothers Big Sisters, and the Veterans League of Long Island; one worker at the Tungsten Thrift Shop, a Miss Azalea McMillan-Gonzalez, took one look at the station wagon (on loan from the Sheriff/Coroner's office) and claimed that most of her stuff was pure junk. Vinyl records, crocheted teapot cozies, cans of tuna fish, and aluminum Jell-O molds. Knitting needles, eye droppers, yellowed pyres of *Ebony* and *Jet.* There were the dozens of library movie fliers the old woman herself had taken time to type and mimeograph, later copy, and even later e-mail to library patrons. But what could you do with a ten-story pile of paper?

Zenobia Malady's mother—herself a youthful ninety-six—visited the grave of her daughter every single day, rain or shine. The old woman herself never transformed into anything other than an old woman,

---

[18]An emotional, intellectual, and near-physical altercation took place when one of the researchers mistakenly called Tungsten Long Island's second oldest Negro community. Why use the word "Negro?" Why lie about the village's status? The first known retired Union soldier came back to spend his twilight years in Tungsten. He wore a jacket decorated with medals. He lived to be 130 years old, and was a candidate for the Guinness World Records, right behind that sucker from Wyandanch who lived to be 131.

[19]Up until 2004 and the next gas war, it was still $4.99 and all-you-can-drink Virgin Bloody Marys.

leaving many to surmise the effects of the Kafkatization were subjective rather than genetically predisposed. Whatever the case, Agnes Malady would not be kept from the final resting place of her only child. It was said that she condoned her daughter's sudden turn toward atheism. And yet Agnes Malady never failed to place little white beads on the grave, perhaps in the hopes that something miraculous might happen, one day.

Sweetness Gore

Mistaken for the longest time for a retarded girl; one of the first people in Tungsten to die, at the age of seventy-seven (decades after her sister Chandra's death), of natural causes. In her life, Sweetness accomplished the following: 1) she began a nonprofit for those suffering PTSD following the effects of Kafkatization; 2) she led tour groups through the old parts of town, the ones officially "not on the map," in an effort to deter gawkers; 3) she legally changed her name to Ellen.

Remained her entire lifetime physiologically impervious to the effects of zombification. When the time came, she allowed herself to be examined "for science purposes only." Married head scientist on committee. Invited to the White House on three occasions.

Just before winning her MacArthur, Ellen Gore printed a page in *The New York Times* in which she asked her former tormentors: *How You Like Me Now????*[20]

Ferris Hardaway

Was convinced that treasure had been buried in the center of Tungsten Proper (right next to the statue of the Union Soldier) and spent much of his adult life attempting to dig it up. Ferris dug and dug, using spades, shovels, and kitchen spoons. His antics were basically the plot of that old movie *God's Little Acre*—where they looked for buried treasure everywhere? Remember? Ferris even claimed that Rex Ingram (the "real" star of the film) was, in fact, his first cousin.

---

[20]And that included all former schoolchildren in Tungsten and Pomegranate Townships.

We loved his tall tales—he was the last of a dying breed, you might say. Spent his sober life selling dyed rabbits' feet and horseshoe silver at a kiosk in the Tungsten Mall.

Once it hit, Ferris' Conversion from Man into Monster was immediate, the fastest on record.[21] With his "new" hands, Ferris clawed his way through his own yard (77 Pallas Street), his aunt's yard (891 Pomegranate Boulevard), his second cousin's yard (57 Ronald Drive) all the way to Revolutionary War-era graves behind the library.[22] He would have gotten farther had not Miss Zenobia Malady spotted him, and tamed his savagely hoodooed heart.

Last seen, the pair was walking down Center Street.

Not in the way you might expect, with arms outstretched and mouths shaped in eternal, monstrous Os. They were quite well mannered. He held her by the elbow and occasionally nipped her chin with his lips. She leaned against him and took deep breaths through her exposed ribs. Their clothes were indeed ragged and smelly, their skulls were showing. But together like that, Malady and Hardaway were the picture of happiness.

If their Translation into "Otherness" was meant to signal the end of the world, it took us all for fools. There would always be a place for tenderness. We knew that. It was also nice to know that May-December relationships were not taboo after the Change; that was some comfort.[23]

---

[21] Again, we hesitate to use such misnomers. The people you saw after the Transformation were the same ones you saw before. You learned to focus on their faces, try to remember who they were and what they owed you or how they hurt you or how much you cared for them in life—and you tried to make that memory stick.

[22] What zombie story would be complete without an old, unkempt graveyard? Contrary to popular belief, the dead never rise from their graves, that is, if you don't count Jesus and a few others from the Good Book. From 1992 through 2012, when Regulatory Efforts were finally achieved, the cemeteries in Tungsten remained relatively quiet places.

[23] Further investigation into Ferris' genealogy led us to uncover certain strange coincidences. Ferris' great grandfather had had his name changed in 1908 from Louis de Ferre to Lewis Ferris, just months after arriving in the United States from Haiti. Louis de Ferre was a Christian man, observing mass at least five times a week his entire life. There is no evidence that he ever practiced voodoo. When asked, the Haitian community members of Tungsten—all three of them— became incensed at the idea that this stereotype had followed them through to this current tragedy. Brookhaven Labs has yet to offer an official apology.

Frank White

Having escaped his father's Biblical hand, as well as his uncle Buddy Boy's televangelical hand (Buddy Boy had not been above appearing on UHF channels to ask for charitable contributions of at least five dollars), Frank White was, at twenty, in his first year at Hofstra University, a place his uncle had told him was the Ivy League of Long Island. Frank White was just literally minding his own business when BLAMMO. Bit in the neck, down like a spinning top.

Would it be overkill to say he didn't see that coming?

Perhaps he should have known in the back of his mind that the old janitor would be coming back. Winston Hall-Miles' teeth hung in his mouth like the gold diggers of 1933. If Frank had only realized that this corpse, this lackluster specimen of the undead, was truly on his last legs,[24] he'd have been able to do away with Mr. Hall-Miles in a one-two punch.

But the darling boy underwent lightning-fast Transmutation. And just when we thought there was a bend in the road for good.

Freedman Witherspoon

Yes, the Change could seem like a blessing to some.

But all his life, he'd had to contend with the "politically correct" name his parents had saddled him with, even before "politically correct" was a phrase in our vocabularies. Supposedly his name originated with his grandmother's grandfather, born in chains in Georgia; after the old man's death, the name "Freedman" became a legacy to pass on from one generation to the next. But of course we wondered why our forebears leaned toward such ham-fisted monikers?[25] Didn't

---

[24]Certain forms of reanimation remain to this day impossible to explain. How had Witherspoon "come back" after the Brookhaven Lab people made sure he was quite "down?" It was speculated that the emotion of revenge and its physiological aftermath had long been underestimated. But if that were the case, we would never see ANYONE pass away, from here until eternity; grudges being a staple of all life as we know it.

[25]Indeed—we have always hated those slave-to-freedom names: Sojourner, Equiano, Box, Booker, Aesop. What the hell? Why has that history of strange names persisted into our present? Who will take us seriously with a name like Hercules or Mingo? If you question this, go ask Mingo Calhoun or Hercules Simpson, of Booth Street and Feather Lane, respectively.

anyone at that point in time find those concoctions overbearing?[26]

Freedman was called "Free" by the people who respected him—the woman who worked in the office of Tungsten Cemetery, where he was Chief Gravedigger. He was called "Freedman" by those in public institutions, like Pomegranate Mercy Hospital and Jugglers Bar and Grille; "Freakman" by evil children walking home from school; "Freedy" by the one woman who devoted herself to him, regardless of the consequences; "Free Free" by her child, who in later years would only have a Fotomat snapshot to remember her father by.

Life went along without too many bumps until he turned thirty-seven, at which point Freedman found himself accused of the murders of two workers at the Horn and Hardart Automat on Tungsten Avenue. You know the place, a pie behind a glass door? It was said that those sorts of places were going out of business; and then this particular one did, and supposedly Freedman entered the place demanding his piece of pecan, and he flipped. Killed the cashiers out of some blind rage, according to witnesses.

We all assumed he was guilty. Just because your name is virtuous doesn't mean you are.[27] We expected an arsenal of knives, rifles, maybe even a canister of tear gas. We didn't know Freedman much beyond his name. We didn't know.

Sheriff Roman led efforts to confront, question, and then kill Freedman.

And after his body was recovered, it was noted that all Freedman had in his pocket was a locket holding a picture of his great-great-great-great grandmother Sindy Hallstrom, field slave to the Hallstroms of Caterwaul, Georgia.

A locket! What kind of grown man carries such a thing? Let alone one accused of murder, guns, and outrage over the demise of the automat?

You would think Kafkatization would have bred a new understanding in people's hearts. But then you would be wrong. Even after he Transmutated, the people of Tungsten were rather unforgiving of Freedman. So what if he had a name as honorable as Martin Luther

---

[26] As a point of fact, Quaysan Fields had wanted to name his first baby D'l'Ondre until his mother Georgia disabused him of that silliness. Before she Passed she insisted on the name Charlton.

[27] We all of us specialize in camouflaged insides.

King? He was a killer, all the same. For no good reason he killed two fine sisters at the Horn and Hardart—we wondered if maybe the ladies at Jugglers would be next? One thing our community really hated was murder for murder's sake. Freedman was a spot on the reputation of all upstanding black people who didn't go around killing every fast girl they wanted to.

People shrugged their shoulders in shame. They came early to Miss Malady's movies and whispered restlessly among themselves in the bathroom, five, six, and seven at a time: *Why did the undead have to be Black in the first place? Ain't we suffered enough?*

Daphine Hammond

Once the captain of the cheerleading squad; once the top-honors graduate of the Long Island School of Beauty; once the first female owner of the first *Car-Bo-Rators* franchise in the county; once the first female from Tungsten to graduate medical school at Stony Brook; once the loving wife of Simon Fields and stepmother to his five children; once a devoted caretaker in the Quarantine Section of Brunswick Hospital.

Lastly, an exceptional watercolor artist of the Great South Bay.

Win Rembert-Walker

Thought about taking up the lynch mob idea years after the demise of Buddy Boy White; even spoke about it through Miss Malady's midnight showing of *Coffy*, where he was hushed many times by the crowd. Went home and organized a vigilante group with his five brothers, calling themselves the Not-Death-Wishes.

We loved us some Win Rembert. Exuberant was a word for him. He filled us with exuberance.

But he died August 2001, just as Brookhaven Labs announced a new and potentially life-saving development in the fight against Kafkatization. Was it a drug, we wondered, a vaccine, a top-secret inoculation that would restore us to normalcy? Talk was rampant, but then petered out, as Brookhaven suddenly began publishing disclaimers in the *Tungsten Gravette*.

Maybe the crops failed, Win Rembert's widow said.

The remaining Not-Death-Wishes went out and tried to rehabilitate a few of the reanimated, with unsuccessful results. A bite on the neck here, a chomp on the leg there. The dead would not rest.

The Not-Death-Wishes claimed to have only goodness in their hearts; indeed, the obituaries that appeared in the *Gravette* all praised the homegrown efforts of an upstanding group of men. Merciful men. Men with female hearts of sympathy. Why did they have to go too?

Calvin, Martin, Richard, and Ralph Rembert were buried alongside their brother Win in the Tungsten Cemetery. None ever tried to leave their final resting grounds, as far as we could tell.

Kai "Skipper" Wilson

Was the final local piece in the Un-Living Puzzle. Toward the end, Brookhaven Labs surrendered to the Higher-Ups in Washington all their files, documents, testimonies, test tubes, beakers, centrifugal results, clandestine photographs, and pertinent and nonpertinent findings. We were neither asked nor told anything. Thereafter, the Scientific Conclusions Committee traveled to laboratories in London, Johannesburg, Sydney. We were instructed to go back to living our normal lives.[28] By then, most of us had already seen countless pill bottles chock full of placebos. We were actually living and breathing just fine, only we didn't know it.

Upon discovering that the remainder of humankind was somehow recovering from the ill effects of Kafkatization—was this the effect of global warming? Subtle movements of the planets?—when we learned that things were going to be all right, that the tide had been turned, we bowed our heads in prayer. Were we like the proverbial phoenixes lifting themselves out of the ashes? Who knew?

Who cared?

After Skipper Wilson passed, there were no more Expirations, no more Cantilevered Completions. There was just the Wait. Then Huge Leaps for Mankind, etc. Regulatory Efforts. An end in sight.

His sister Linnea had been the first to find him dead, in their backyard garden on Douglas Boulevard, and she collapsed and nearly died

---

[28]When pressed, the Interpol man said: Are you that clueless? This has never just been a Tungsten thing.

herself from grief; days later, she watched as her brother's remains were rocketed into outer space by NASA.

She went to the authorities with questions about the wild "black" yonder.

Never you mind, was the official line. Keep on keeping on.

"He was such a good person," she muttered over and over—a standard phrase in those days. "Why did he have to go? Skipper was on the verge."

On the verge. That phrase remained a mystery for years. Of course, modern science always has a way of figuring out and curing everything, from racism to sexism to disease to gas supplies to war to suicide. We sometimes wonder if Skipper simply grew wings and traveled to heaven? Or if he began renewed life as an oak in Tungsten Park? Or if he caught sight of a new and remote planet, and decided to set up camp there? We'll never know for sure. We can only use our brains.

Because, among other things, Modern Science has taught us the obvious: before they were zombies, they were us, and we were them. How could we forget that—even for (as the Poet once said) "the least division of an hour?"

After rescue from the nightmare was imminent; after we came to our senses; after the world stopped and looked and listened—something amazing happened. Do you remember? Houses were no longer burned, and hands could touch without fear of contamination. We could kiss without latex, touch without hot water. Love without tears.

Something amazing had happened.

But it was not an earth-shattering surprise for most of us (when you thought about it), the rediscovery of our similarity to each other, whether dead or alive. This rediscovery was like the tiniest insect's wing under a microscope.

It truly rocked our world.

V.V. GANESHANANTHAN

K Becomes K

I recently went to an appointment with a terrorist I used to know. He lives near me in New York City, and when he wrote me a letter that said *Dear Sashi, come and see me,* without thinking very much about it, I did. Even when I was a little girl in Sri Lanka, before I had ever heard the word *terrorist,* I knew that when a certain kind of person wanted something, you did it without asking a lot of questions. I met a lot of these sorts of people when I was younger because I used to be what you would call a terrorist myself.

I helped these people for a friend, and I left them for the same reason. So you must understand: I am not an unlikable person, and neither are all terrorists. That word, *terrorist,* is too simple for the people I have known. It is too simple for me, too simple even for this man. How could one word be enough? But you asked me a question, so I am going to say it anyway, because it is the language you know, and it will help you to understand who we were, what we were called, and who we have really become.

We begin with this word. But I promise that you will come to see that it cannot contain everything that has happened. And while I am no longer the version of myself who met with terrorists every day, I also want you to know that when I was that woman, when two terrorists encountered each other in my world, what they said first was simply *hello.* Like any two people you might know or love.

I met the first terrorist I knew at the precise time in his life when he was deciding to become one. In 1981, when I met K, I was almost fourteen years old. He and his family lived down the road from me and mine, in one village of a Tamil town called Jaffna, in Sri Lanka. The Jaffna peninsula is the northernmost part of the island. Many people have died there: some killed by the Sri Lankan Army, some by the Indian Peace Keeping Forces, and some by the Tamil separatists, whom you know as the terrorists.

In the village where we were born, everyone was related to, hated, and loved by everyone else. In that heat, we needed and worked for each other. Now that I have lived through more than twenty seasons of snow, I dream of the village heat mostly in terms of fever. Some women carried cheap umbrellas to protect their faces from the sun. But the heat was not only outside us—we created it too. Our mothers cooked over wood stoves in hot kitchens, and we boiled water for tea almost hourly. We lit oil lamps before our household shrines and touched torches to roadside refuse. We mourned around burning pyres, undaunted. If we had let the heat faze us, we would not have survived. And we did more than survive, truly: we studied. I wanted to become a doctor. K wanted to become a doctor. And this was what made us alike.

He had the upper hand from the first, not because he was older, or a boy, but because I began as his patient. On the morning that we met, I was boiling water for tea. I had to use a piece of cloth to hold the pot to avoid burning myself. But that morning, the cloth slipped, the handle slipped, and the pot slipped, pouring scalding water all over me. I screamed and screamed for my mother—*Amma!* My high, shrill voice carried out onto the road, where K was passing. Hearing my cry, he swiftly stopped, let his bicycle fall in the dirt at our gate, and ran inside.

By the time he reached me in the kitchen, Amma had already found me. I screamed and cried and called every god I could name. Bubbles rose and popped on my skin. I could hear myself boiling and blistering, and looking down at myself, I could see it. Amma was sobbing, too horrified to move.

"Sit!" he said, and pointed to a chair. When I kept screaming, he pushed me down into the chair and peeled my blouse up, baring my hot stomach. I heard Amma's cry of *aiyo!* as though from a great distance. Snatching a bowl of eggs off the table, K began cracking them onto the burns. Her eyes widening, Amma moved forward as though to stop him.

"It will cool the burn," he said quickly, blocking her.

Trying to master the pain, I tried to focus on anything but the wounds. I stared at him and saw only his thumbs, working in and out of the eggshells, scraping the slime of the whites out cleanly and onto the swelling rawness of the burn. He did it very quickly, as though he had had a lot of practice, as though he were making a cake and every precious scrap of egg were going to be eaten. I remember those thumbs, and I remember the eggs—they were so cold, and my skin was so hot, so hot that I cannot quite believe that the eggs did not just cook on my flesh. He was right—it did help. When the last of the six eggs was cracked and cooling on my skin, K looked up at Amma.

"Are there more?"

"What?"

"More eggs?" She blinked, then nodded. "Good—cover the burn with a few more. The doctor—I should go—"

When K came back with the doctor half an hour later, I had finally stopped crying. The doctor looked over the makeshift dressing with approval. "Whose idea was this?" he asked.

"His," Amma said.

So I began as his patient, though he ended as mine.

So many foods remind me of K now. He is on each wiped plate and inside each cold glass; each cup of hot milk tea with sugar is one he refused. The eggs I make myself each morning, Tabasco or Clancy's Fancy hot sauce sliding bloodily across the top, are the ones he cracked onto my body. His family gave me varieties of fruit that are unattainable or tasteless in this country. When he came to visit me a few days later, his aunt came with him, bearing my favorite *mampalam*—mangoes—and *valaipalam,* the special, small, sweet bananas that grew in their yard. My mother must have mentioned that I liked them. The fruit pleased me, but for once, I felt more interested in the strange boy, who until this moment had belonged more to my brothers, his schoolmates, than to me. I tried to examine him without being too obvious about it. His shirt was tucked unevenly into his trousers, which were too large for his body. He looked sturdy, but not skinny, and he had a rim of hair on his upper lip that was not quite a mustache. It barely showed—he was dark from the sun, even though as an asthmatic, he had not been allowed outside very much. He had thick spectacles, which he took off and wiped carefully with a handkerchief. A woman's handkerchief, I noticed. Later, I learned that it had belonged to his late mother.

While he polished his spectacles, I took a good look at his face. He had a thin nose, a full mouth, and a high forehead with a gently curved widow's peak, which might have accounted for his seeming older than sixteen despite the lack of facial hair. Most boys that age in our village had mustaches, my brothers included. K could not seem to manage one.

But behind the spectacles, his eyes were lovely and old, full of a certainty that appealed to me. I wanted that certainty for myself, to be someone who could look at burned flesh and not hesitate to touch it.

He replaced his spectacles, and when I realized that he was studying me with equal intensity I looked away.

His aunt fussed over me, and my mother let me off from the usual duty of serving them tea. I had never done it with the appropriate grace, and the burn, stiffening, made me move even more awkwardly than I did naturally. Instead, I sat and talked to his aunt as he continued to study me. Finally, she and my mother stopped talking about the near-tragedy and began talking about the upcoming temple festival. K looked over at my mother and his aunt, who were deep in conversation, and then back at me. The thick lenses distorted his eyes, but it was too late: I already knew they were lovely.

"So. How are you feeling now?"

"I hardly knew you were there," I said. "It hurt that much."

He would teach me, later, to lie about what hurt and how much. Most women, he would say, are naturally much better liars than you.

"And now?"

"Now? Better. But it itches," I said, plucking at my blouse. "How did you know what to do?" I had had time, in the intervening days, to become curious about the science of what he had done.

He shrugged. "It made sense, even though it wasn't modern. The protein and fat of the egg soothe the burn."

"Thank you," I said awkwardly.

"Don't scratch it—you'll get a scar."

I moved my hand away from my stomach, and we sat in silence for a moment.

"Are your brothers here?" he asked finally.

"No," I said.

"Oh."

I took that to mean that his aunt had made him come with her to visit me, that he had little use for girls and little use for me. So we were not friends at first, although he had already been more intimate with me than any other boy I had known. I frowned when I thought about that, about his peeling the blouse away from my skin, about how that skin had looked when he had done it. He had not seemed at all taken aback by the sight of the wound, the volcanic molten look of it.

I admired that steadiness. But I was also embarrassed by the recollection of the nakedness of my pain. His certain hands had touched me as though it was not an intrusion, as though it came naturally, although during that moment of looking down at my own body, I had been horrified at the sight of myself. His sureness made me wonder what it would take to horrify him.

Although we had already had that intimacy, although certain barriers of propriety had been breached, it had been a forced breach required by the circumstances, and friendship did not come easily to us. We would have to go out of our respective ways to become friends, and I was not, at first, inclined to go out of my way. I was embarrassed, and I did not like feeling obliged to someone I considered a stranger. Our paths had crossed rarely. He was two years older than me; he went to the famous Jaffna Hindu College. He belonged to my brothers, after all, and he was a boy, and therefore our friendship was unlikely. Even when I saw him at the temple, we were separated by the traditional divide between men and women.

The next time we saw each other was at the temple, in fact. I saw that his mustache appeared slightly more successful, and noticed his quick glance at my belly, where one of my mother's old sari blouses covered the bandages from the burn. Suddenly conscious of new breasts, I lowered my arm across my body and looked away. The mustache looked foolish to me. He was not unusual, standing among the line of men waiting to be blessed. You, you American, you would have thought him just one of many dark men with white smiles. And, you know, you would have been wrong.

K died on a September morning in 1987, on a stage that had been specially built for him to do so. It was outside the Nallur Kandaswamy Hindu temple, one of the temples of my childhood, and his childhood—one of our holiest and most loved places. At the time of his death he had not taken food or even water for eleven days. It was the morning of the twelfth day of what was being called his *satyagraha*. A word that refers to the tactic of nonviolence that Mahatma Gandhi originated.

He died at 8:37 a.m., at the age of twenty-one, with a rebel's name that was different from the one with which he had been born and with which I had loved him. It was a Saturday. Today Tiger supporters around the world mark this time as a holy hour, but I can tell you that at the moment of his death K was still an ordinary man—just a grown-up version of the boy who had lived down the road from me in our village. His death made him no more saintly than he had been in life, which is to say not very. He was neither more moral nor more honest than the governments he protested. If anything, he was less so, and this made it harder to let him die, because I resented his death more. It was worse to mourn him, knowing truly what he had done. His face was harder to look at and to love, which I already did. Hunger had carved new hollows out of it. His mustache had wilted over his cracked mouth, shielding it from sight. He looked older and more austere. If I had not known already that it was K, I might not have recognized his body. When I bathed him each night with a wet cloth, it was like touching a stranger. While in many ways he did resemble the boy who had been my friend, in its hunger and thirst his body had traveled a great distance from its previous self. Perhaps I should say that he looked as he might have looked in fifty years, had he lived—and never fasted.

K and our superiors had chosen this hunger strike as a method of protest against the government of India, which in its attempt at peacekeeping had instead become embroiled in our war. Forty years after Gandhi, in Sri Lanka, the Indian army occupied Tamil homes, crowded Tamil villages, raped Tamil women, and burned Tamil houses. They had burned his not so long ago. The occasion for K's decision to fast was an India-sponsored accord that he believed ignored the Tamil interest in a homeland. Both he and I were connected to the movement, the Liberation Tigers of Tamil Eelam, the Tamil Tigers, which for years had used violence and guerrilla warfare against the Sri Lankan government. That government discriminated against Tamils, but our own dubious morality was not lost on me. No one I knew in the movement would have dared to say such a thing aloud. At the same time, I understood that no act of violence we had committed had ever attracted as much support for a homeland as the act of violence K committed now, on his own body.

Thousands and thousands of people crowded all around us. I felt both alone and the desire to be alone. I could not count how many people there were around us, but I did not know any of them the way I knew him. There might have been as many as a hundred thousand. People swarmed, clinging to each other and to the stage's edge. When they came too close to me, I fought down an unreasonable alarm. They meant no harm, but they were hungry for him even as his body consumed itself. Many of them had been fasting in solidarity with him. Like him, some of them were also performers and opportunists. Our leaders had scattered speakers and microphones through the crowd, and for days, people had taken turns standing in front of them and crying out their grievances. Their eyes looked dull and enormous, rimmed with red. Now, after days of noise and threats of disruption, the temple was finally silent. The speakers hummed only with wind. No one knew what would happen at the moment of death. There had been rumors of rioting and calls for blood. For the moment, we felt only a terrible sense of anticipation made of both eagerness and fear.

I myself stood on the stage with K's doctor, the Tiger physician with whom I worked. I shook a little and tried to hold myself very straight. It was hot—very, very hot, and I had been standing there since sunrise, when I had gotten up from where I slept near K. I looked down at him where he lay on the floor of the stage, surrounded by the flags of the Tigers. I had known and watched the rhythm of his breathing for years in private. To do the same in public felt like a violation, but the irresistible rhythm of habit compelled me: his chest rose, his chest fell, his chest rose, his chest fell. His glasses slid askew, more askew with each slow breath, his eyes closed under them as though he were just nodding off on his veranda at home. His chest rose; his chest stilled, and once more I anticipated its descent. I waited, and the space of that wait grew infinite.

If you had asked me immediately afterward what I did as he died, I would have told you that I bent down to touch my forehead to his, that his skin felt warm and dry, that he still smelled faintly of *iluppai* flowers and other growing, living things. I would have told you that I went with him into the endless country of that trapped breath, a place where neither of us could cry out or make any human sound. I would have told you that although I had known that he would die—known it, perhaps, from the first time I had chosen to help him—that although this was the seed that had been planted, and watered, and planned for, in the face of its bloom, the air stopped in my throat too, and I could not believe what we had done.

Later, other people told me that when he died, I did not touch him: I stood apart from him on the stand and moved my hand to my mouth as if to silence myself.

The doctor put his hand on my elbow, which was wet with perspiration.

"Sashi," he said. "Sashi."

And then I breathed again, and K did not. It was the first moment in which such a thing was possible, and the sharp quickening pain of it stunned me. How swiftly the world reshaped itself around his absence! Perhaps someone you know has died and you have a sense of what I mean: the horror of knowing that everything is going to continue very nearly as it did before. People will do their jobs; you will even do yours, although you did not know that you were capable of it.

Everything in medicine has its order, and this is also true of death: it has to be announced, the hour marked and recorded. The doctor, I understood, was going to pronounce it. I was glad to be spared this; even steeled as I had been for days against this inevitability, it would have been a very permanent thing to have the declaration of K's passing be something that came from my mouth. And it was a moment for the spotlight, which suited the doctor and did not suit me. I watched him play to the tense and waiting theater of people, as I would not have done. He leaned down over the prone body of my friend and with an exaggerated motion, put two fingers to the curve of K's dry neck, and then to the inside of his dry wrist. I had never imagined that someone could be so utterly parched. K looked as though, were he to be cut open, he would not even bleed.

The doctor sighed and looked up at me, and then at K's father, who was standing next to me. The doctor touched his own eyes and drew his fingers down his face, mimicking the motion of tears. As if he had been waiting for a cue, or for permission, K's father began to cry. The doctor turned to the crowd and made the same motion, and as though they were a great chorus, they wept in unison, keening and wailing and mourning. It was a peaceful mourning during which no one threw a stone, fired a gun, or lit a match. Despite what we had anticipated, there was no visible anger—only an unquenchable grief that washed the tension away. In the distance, at the far end of the temple grounds, the cadres began to move out. They had been instructed to occupy and protect property that otherwise would be at risk for destruction. Several vans took off from the temple. They would travel through Jaffna town. Voices through distant megaphones, spreading the news and asking for calm. Above the weeping audience, the beautiful crows circled. They, too, had been waiting for days, but now they swooped away from us, higher and higher, their paths looping upward like incense smoke.

Four cadres who had been waiting with K lifted him from the dais and the people's cries around us grew louder. His sarong fell around his limp legs, and they looked even thinner. Behind his plain checked shirt, the red flag of the Tigers was the biggest and brightest spot in the crowd, which had arrived wearing white in a preemptive strike at lamenting him. I thought that if I touched him now he might turn to powder. We might all ignite. I wanted to step down off the platform and tell them that I had loved K, that he had been the friend of my life. I wanted the people beside the stage to be with me, and I wanted to be with them, but the difference in our grief separated us. They looked like me and spoke my language and had grown up in the same places, but they were mourning for someone else.

The Nallur temple was the most beautiful of all the Hindu temples in Jaffna, and arguably, of all the Hindu temples in Sri Lanka: a good place for K to die, to make his last gesture, not least because it was dedicated to Murugan, the god of war, to whom K had always shown particular devotion. K's body was carried inside the temple, and the doctor and I followed. As we moved across the stage toward the temple awning, we met the smell of jasmine and incense, and the burnt, clean odor I had associated with holiness from childhood. They bore his body down the steps to the awning and through the main corridor, which was a passage both wide and long. It felt like the death procession of a king. Above my head the bells of the clock in the main tower sounded. Around the clock, carved figures of temple guardians and gods watched over us. He could not have chosen a grander theater.

The priests awaited us. They, too, cried with great ostentation and decorum. One of them came forward to usher us from the main chamber into a side room, where the cadres left the doctor and me with the body. The door closed behind them with a quiet click, and I looked down at K's dead face. It was kinder in death. Although he had been unconscious with his eyes closed when he died, they had fallen open somehow as he was carried in. Even glassed with death, they were beautiful eyes, still full of a scholar's quiet civilization, as though he were tired from a long night in the university library. Reaching under his glasses, I closed them with a shudder at the desert tenderness of his eyelids and the long, brittle brush of his lashes. The doctor undressed him quickly. When he motioned to me to look away from the naked body, I ignored him. I did not want to be spared anything about this body, the ugliness and horror of each wasted muscle. K's skin flaked and peeled as the doctor began to prepare the body for the funeral cortege. Little pieces of him drifted to the floor. His scalp littered his bushy black hair with sandy pieces of his crumbling. I squatted and watched, completely still. When the doctor asked if I was all right, I nodded. But I could not bear how K looked. I rose and went to ask one of the priests for a bowl of oil. When I returned, without my asking, the doctor stopped his preparations of the body.

The oil smelled familiarly of coconut. They used this same oil to bathe the gods and light the lamps in this temple. It had a good fragrance with which to send K away: clean and spicy. He had liked this smell. I myself associated it with *dharshan,* the aspect of holiness we all wished to acquire when we entered a temple. Squatting back down, I dipped the edge of my white cotton sari into the oil and began to smooth it over the body. I drew the sari over his head like a veil, and the oil dripped from the corner of fabric onto his head. I let the sari drop from my hand, closed my eyes, and put my hands into his shock of hair like a pair of combs. His hair was dull, filled with windblown dust, tangled and matted from twelve days without brushing. Moisture without life seeped back into him. I looked up at the doctor, who nodded. "It will look a little better," he said. "They know how he died. They watched it."

And now he watched me. But I barely noticed. It felt like a ritual, but it was something I had never done before and have never done again for anyone. I put my fingers directly into the bowl of oil and touched K's eyebrows, which were standing up, wild with bristly hairs. I smoothed them down. Without wiping my hands clean, I took off his glasses, marking them with oily prints. I stroked his eyelids again, and under his eyes where the circles were. I tugged his cheeks and his earlobes and rounded his chin. Behind me, the door clicked. The doctor was gone. At last, after so many years, I was alone again with K.

I pushed a finger between his teeth and pulled it out again, still dry from his sandpaper tongue. I was not K's wife, or his sister, or his mother, but I poured oil from the bowl so that it formed a pool on the crater of his shallow chest. I pushed it up, into his neck and onto his withered arms, so far from the guns they had carried and the grenades they had thrown. I was not K's doctor, and I was not his lover, but I put my thumbs into his elbows and cupped my hands around their edges, which were sharper than his bones as I had previously known them. I undid the knot of my long hair. Kneeling, I laid my temple next to his shoulder and found that as I had always suspected, my head fit into a perfect place his joints made for me. I stretched myself out next to him. Beneath me, the concrete floor of the temple was cool. I moved onto him, matching each of my living parts against his dead ones so that my whole self was pressed against him, living cells against dead cells. He was still warm. Tall as I was, there was almost no difference between us. My hair fell forward and across his body, dead cells on dead cells. I let my nails cut into his back. I felt rather than saw the quiet fold of his once-skinny stomach, now bloated with hunger. I held onto him with all my might, as though I could bury myself in him, or as though between us, the earth and I could still hurt him.

It was not erotic, not even a little. It was not romantic, not even a little. It was desperate. For the first time in my life, I wanted to die. I dipped my finger into the oil and put it on my own dry lips. It tasted sour. I wanted to soak into him, to fill up each crevice and hollow bone, so I kissed him with that flammable mouth, but even with the oil, it was a chaste, paper-lipped kiss that came too late. Pushing myself up, I found that my sari was drenched in the oil I had placed on his body to give it the appearance of life. The scars on his stomach, which had been barely visible before, shone brightly, pushed into sharp relief by the edema of his fast. They were the scars of a battle he had fought in May, in Vadamarachchi, where he had been badly wounded. My hands mapped the damage, and finally, I touched my friend, no longer my patient. The marks began on his right side and traveled above his navel, ending on the left side of his rib cage. Doctors had removed parts of his liver and intestines. He had nearly died and in defiance of the code of our movement, I had wept then as I could not now. My own stomach scar-less, the broken eggs of two childhoods ago still sliding invisibly across it.

The scars reminded me that no matter what was done to K's body, the crowd had already seen things as the Tigers wished them to be seen. The scars would be covered up. He would be anointed with more oil and garlanded. He would be marked with sweet ash and saffron paste and *kungumum*, the red powder. His body would move through the streets and villages of Jaffna like the statue of a god, and no one would dare to say that he had never been a believer in true nonviolence. They would say that he was greater than Gandhi, and he was not. Only my hands had on them the detritus of his skin.

I rose from K's body.

When doctor and priests finished their work, I dressed K in the uniform they gave me, the uniform of a lieutenant colonel. He had received a promotion upon his death, just as though he had died in battle. It made no difference to them how he died, just as it had made no difference to him. But it mattered to me.

I buttoned up his dear body in its brown shirt, latched his belt around his waist, pulled up the zipper of his trousers, and straightened his medals. The doctor let me do all of this. It was not the work of a doctor, but the work of a woman, and although I was not yet a doctor, I was no longer a child. He handed me the Tiger sash, and I draped it around K's shoulders, my fingers shaking. I took the camera K had given me for my sixteenth birthday out of my black bag and snapped a picture of him for the last time. I did it slowly, adjusting the angle of his uplifted chin, tracing his eyebrows again, moving his hat so that the shadows it cast would not obscure his eyes, even though his closed lids hid their light. I took my time, tucking his hair behind his ears and refolding his collar so that I could touch him again. I resisted—just barely—the urge to shake him.

Finally, the four male cadres came again and took his body away from me. They placed him into an open casket made of wood. Already, despite the doctor's care, K's hands were beginning to curl and freeze. His back stiffened, and already he was a stranger. Already he belonged to people who did not know him, and I could not believe I had ever laid my head against those unwelcoming shoulders. The cadres moved to put K's open coffin into the back of a black Jeep, and the crowd, wailing, followed it on foot. They formed a gruesome trail of white. I lingered at the end of the crowd, along with the doctor. The breeze that blew at my oily sari did not cool the Jaffna heat.

As we passed into the town, we saw house after house already festooned with the plaits of coconut leaves, a symbol of mourning. From other temples and schools we could hear funeral music blasting with obscene volume and pompousness. In front of all the houses, we saw pictures of K, garlanded and lit by oil lamps. At each town, people came out to join the train of mourners. Bare feet kicked up the dust of the road, and from far away, villages could see us coming by the cloud we brought with us. The weeping rang so loud that it carried across farms and across paddy fields, to beaches and lagoons, over the entire peninsula. Tears arrived, knocked on doors, and were met with open and regretful arms. Sorrow took up residence in every street of every borough.

K died as he had done everything in the last years of his life: with a great sense of theater. He could have been an actor, I see now, but even in times of peace, when more Jaffna men chose professions other than death-making or peace-making, they were rarely actors. It was not respectable to admit to acting. It would not have been respectable for him to admit to it during the fast. But even in the last days, when he did not have much strength left, I could tell by the exaggerated and slow way that he was moving that he had more than he was willing to show. He wanted to make the end a climax, and around him the propaganda machine that he had constructed whirred and clicked to help him. Cameramen focused on him. The thrum of music and the shrill voices of women singing rose to a higher pitch as though he had cued it. The priests, whose order was never disturbed, stopped even their slow, measured movements. In the distance, we could smell fires burning, the smell which is constantly in the air in Sri Lanka. It is the fragrance of purification, an ongoing process, and it smells not bad, but painful.

"I go only to return," he had said to me before closing his eyes: the traditional farewell. "Go and come back," I answered: the traditional answer. And although I have told you this story in English, you must remember, we were in Tamil. A private language for me now, here, and I remember him saying that as though it were private, as though it were not only to me but only for me, although we were surrounded by so many other people. And even as he said it, I was still wading through the river of my own understanding. He should have died days earlier. He was missing parts of his body. Death by fasting should not have taken him longer than a week. I had a suspicion that they had somehow stretched it out on purpose. For show. He went to sleep, but no one else could. Around the crowd, televisions had been set up. They were broadcasting only one channel, the channel of the Tigers, which was called Nidarshanam. I remember looking up to the screen, where the twin heads of K and Gandhi shone out at me. As I watched, the two heads moved closer together, merged, and blended into one. I could hear a group of women beginning a set of *thevaram,* devotional songs. Air rose from deep inside me, and I breathed heavily to expel it. I gulped, and swallowed, and started to laugh. I could not help it. K's mustache on Gandhi's face did not fit at all. Gandhi's protruding ears instead of K's obedient ones made no sense. It was funny—it was funny. I laughed as quietly as I could, which was not very quietly, and wiped my face, which was not wet, with the backs of my hands.

In a time of peace, as a Hindu, K would have been cremated. On a funeral pyre he would have burst and sparked like tinder. He would have risen into the air as smoke. If he had had a son, the boy would have carried the torch to light the flame. Since he had no son, his father would have done the deed. Since he had no wife, only his friends would have borne witness.

Only his friends. I could say that he was only a friend, but that would not be true; that would not be right. Our friendship exceeds and surpasses, expands and embraces. K is more, always; he is with me still. Here in the West, people think women of my country leap into fire with the bodies of men we have loved. But he was only a friend—*only*—and I let him go. They took his body from me, but it did not matter. Do you see now? Do you understand? In K, I had and lost such a friend that I became the place where his body burned.

TRAVIS HOLLAND
Planet of Fear

Here was my Wednesday ten o'clock: Robert James Coates, according to the file on my desk. But he refused to answer to that name, and at our first meeting, after the guard left us alone, insisted I call him *Dog*, which naturally I wouldn't do. "All right, then, whatever, call me D," he said agreeably, as if it hardly mattered anyway, what name he went by. He had a way of smiling, I noticed almost right away, slyly and yet with a measure of sad tolerance, that made me want to check my shirt collar for stains. By our third meeting, he was calling himself *Tick*.

"What is it with you and dogs?" I asked.

"Naw, man. Like a clock and shit. You know, tick-tock?"

"Interesting," I said, pretending not to notice the bruises on his face. But in my session notes I'd already written: *Talk to Fuentes about moving this kid out of the stacks. Big fish eat little fish.* The JDC was notorious for being something of a farm league for the sprawling adult state prison up north; obviously some kid had soured on Tick. It was my job, if job is the proper word for what I did, to shepherd through minnows like Tick—the baffled masses, as my wife, Julie, called them.

"So, *Tick.* What's new? You making friends?"

Tick pursed his swollen lips, blowing a raspberry. He'd brought along a paperback book, *Planet of Fear,* which I would let him read as soon as we'd gotten through the requisite back-and-forth. "That's me," Tick said, "Mr. Friendly. I guess I just got that kind of face."

"Oh? What kind's that?"

"You know. The punching kind."

He was small, even for fifteen, and upon processing had opted for the short clippers, probably hoping a shaved head would make him look menacing. A bad choice: he looked more like a shorn sheep than a gladiator, and reminded me of an old photograph I'd once found pinned to the corkboard above my father's desk, some wretchedly thin, hollow-eyed factory kid in East London, surprised at his metal press by the photographer's roaring flash.

"Anyway," Tick said, and tapped the book against his knee, "I got in a few shots. I mean, you got to, right?"

"Sometimes," I said. Not exactly the sort of concession you'd expect from a youth counselor, but if I'd learned anything here, it was this: you have to clamber for whatever handhold you can find with these kids, however small. And I liked Tick. Right away I'd sensed glints of promise in him, a bumbling, disordered but ultimately humane intelligence under that disastrously shaved head with its nicks and old scars. A thief, yes—he had hotwired his first car at thirteen—but harmless. "Look, I'm gonna try and get you out of the stacks," I told him now, and wished immediately I'd waited until after I'd spoken to the supervisor in charge of Tick's quad, Fuentes, with whom I'd lately had zero luck. The stacks were what the common cells were called, big bare rooms in which upwards of a dozen bunk beds were crammed together, and where, at night, after lights-out, the lordlings and their pumped-up soldiers reigned. "I can't promise anything," I added.

Tick shrugged. He'd resisted opening *Planet of Fear*, but I could feel his attention bending that way, a bookish, not necessarily impolite withdrawing. We'd agreed to my letting him read in my office during our counseling time after I'd noticed him sitting with a book by himself in the quad one day not long after our first meeting, an island of intense calm in all that rollicking noise. As libraries go, ours was a disgrace even by the truncated standards of Florida youth correction: a handful of milk crates heavy with yard sale paperbacks, which a guard would lock up every night in the janitor's closet, and which, collectively, gave off a sour, hopeless odor I'd lately come to associate with my father, strangely enough. Of course, my father wouldn't have been caught dead with a book like *Planet of Fear*, mass market sci-fi being, for him, vaguely on par with porn. Fiction of any kind he had little use for, and on the afternoons I read to him, my father would snort and stamp like a pastured racehorse that still feels, somewhere deep within itself, the dim stirring of old strength. "Oh, Tuchman wasn't without her gifts," he commented after our last visit—lately we'd been plowing through *A Distant Mirror*, that litany of medieval woe and calamity. As a graduate student in London, he once met the famous Barbara Tuchman at a party, a few years before she died. And did she leave any impression on him? "Not even a whisper," my father said.

"So you gonna ask me about my name?" Tick said.

"You want me to?"

"That's your job, isn't it? Figuring out us hood rats. So you can fix us."

I looked down at my notes. Apart from that reminder to talk to Fuentes, I had nothing of consequence to offer, at least in terms Tick might appreciate. I certainly couldn't protect him. Across my desk, where the sunlight filtered in through the big palm tree outside, a shoal of lambent, knife-shaped shadows blurred and swayed; in my imagination, I sometimes heard the soft steady *snip-snip* of scissors: all those minutes and hours I'd spent in this office and would never get back, my life, right there.

"All right," I said finally. "What's with the new name?"

But Tick must have caught the fluttering tail-end of my thoughts, because he scowled now, in his clownish, forgiving way, twisting up that sharp face of his as if I'd farted. "Shit, I don't know," he said. "Better than *Rob*ert, I guess. Might as well write *punch me* here." He drew a finger sharply across his forehead. "My mom just named me that so I'd know who my dad was."

"Where's he?"

"Dead. Got himself blasted trying to jack some 7-Eleven. He'd already robbed the place the week before."

"I'm sorry to hear that," I said.

Tick shrugged philosophically. "Dude lacked imagination, I guess."

For the twenty minutes that remained we didn't speak. Tick read, slouched in the chair before my desk, and I wrote up my notes on the computer, then studied the shadows on my desk. When the guard knocked on the door and Tick stood up, I said, "Keep your head down."

"Man; that's all I do."

Later, as I was going out for coffee, I looked for him. He was sitting on the floor in the quad, his skinny legs in the rolled-up jumpsuit stuck out in front of him, reading. I'd e-mailed Fuentes and by then received his no. As I watched, a boy sauntered past the scratched shatterproof glass. He had a dark blue tattoo on his big bicep, homemade and crooked: *Tony.* Eyes lifted innocently to the wire-covered skylights, he had his hands clasped behind his back in a pose of contented power. One of the lordlings, I thought. He seemed to steer directly toward Tick, as if an invisible wire stretched between them. When he kicked Tick's outstretched feet and then tore the book from his hands, flinging it away, I felt my own heart lurch, a sickening drop.

*

From the JDC I drove to my parents' house. "Be nice, he's had a rough day," my mother said, letting me inside.

My father was in his study. A glass of Four Roses waited for me on the desk next to *A Distant Mirror*. "The collapse continues," my father said almost cheerfully when I lifted it and drank. By this he meant a more general collapse, I understood, not just his own. Until nine months ago he had been a professor of English history at the University of Miami, and a lifetime of addressing bored undergrads had left him hamstrung with a penchant for dramatic overstatement, along with the certainty that human civilization was cartwheeling toward the grave. He was standing by the window at his old lectern, which he'd stolen in a fit of drunken pique after his retirement dinner, demanding I somehow fit the thing into my Subaru. Which I did, loyal son that I am. "And how's Miss Tuchman today?" I asked, picking up the book.

"Oh, she's dead."

"What from this time? The garrote? Poisoning?"

"Plague," my father said.

This had become our usual shtick. In the twelve months since his diagnosis, my father had begun to see himself in almost everything I read to him. One week he might be Caesar, slipping in his own blood on the Senate steps, another week Pepys, calmly watching London burn. Perhaps unsurprisingly, with all this historical mayhem went a fair amount of bourbon, although my mother would always at some point bring me a glass of mineral water, as if she'd been listening in the hallway, waiting for my voice to crack. In the silences when I paused, with the air conditioner burbling away outside, I'd glance at my father, perched like an examiner at his lectern, and check his face for signs of confusion or fear. For all its mysterious origins, Botkin's is ruthlessly efficient in its progression, and with my father, the disease had plodded along in its usual uninspired way, ticking off the check-boxes. Within a month of his first symptoms, my father's handwriting had deteriorated to gibberish. Two months, and he could no longer add or subtract simple numbers. The latest indignity—but not the last, we had been warned—had been the loss of his ability to read. Yet through it all, he had remained himself. Which is to say, largely insufferable.

"In October 1347," I read, "two months after the fall of Calais, Genoese trading ships put into the harbor of Messina in Sicily with dead and dying men at the oars."

"And we're off," my father said.

He often interrupted like this—little notes flung into the air. Sometimes he would make me reread some line or passage, and when I did, his long, soft-featured face, normally so tight with secret griefs, would take on a dreamy, almost serene aspect. Damp, dull England had been for him a kitchen garden from which to launch himself into the world, Midwestern remoteness burnished to a good, durable polish, and so watching his slow collapse was like watching the gradual disintegration of a once-imposing but now mostly disregarded monument. He had broken down crying once, weeks earlier, as I was reading a description of Mao's Great Leap Forward—all those starving peasants stationed like props with their rakes and hoes along the tracks for the Chairman to see as his train roared past. When I tried to comfort him, he waved me back furiously. "For God's sake, just stop talking. You sound like an inspirational calendar." Later, though, as I was leaving, he let me hug him. I remember being unexpectedly shaken by the smell of his skin lotion, its faintly acidic, babyish sweetness.

At home, I picked over the dinner plate Julie had left for me in the fridge. She and our five-year-old daughter, Sofia, were in the living room, watching television. They'd hollered hello when I came in, and now Sofia swept into the kitchen and demanded I make her spell her name. "All right, spell your name," I said.

"S-O-F-I-A: Sofia."

"Amazing, honey."

"And Dad? We have to go on a nature walk tonight and look at bugs. I'm supposed to." Sofia had started kindergarten three months earlier, and still treated every offhand suggestion by her teacher, the all-knowing Mrs. Martinson, as a sacrosanct commandment. It was cute, if a bit unnerving at times, this priestly devotion. Every few days, she arrived home from school bearing armloads of artwork, erratically colored but earnest and cheerful, which Julie and I made room for on the bulletin board.

Julie came in and kissed me, her lips brushing my hair. She'd changed out of her nurse scrubs—she owned half a dozen different pairs, all purple, which she insisted on washing separately from our clothes. "You want some meth-head's piss getting washed with your nice shirts and underwear?" she'd asked once. "Because that's *my* day, man. Piss, blood, puke. All your assorted human muck." Through the kitchen window, I could see Sofia's plastic wading pool with its ring of cavorting and stoned-looking ducks. Days of fierce rain and unseasonably scalding heat had turned it into a swamp-colored petri dish. "How's your dad?" Julie asked after Sofia had gone back to her cartoons.

"Still a dick."

"Be nice."

"Why does everyone keep telling me that?"

Julie glanced at the bulletin board. "Do they?" she asked innocently. "Well, you could always pretend he's one of your boys. Pelt him with sympathy until he cracks."

I looked out at Sofia's pool. "I am nice," I said. "I just spent an hour reading to a man who thinks the Black Death *underperformed*. His words. I got kids showing up for counseling all beat up. I have to deal with his bullshit too?"

"Seems you do," Julie said.

Even into November the days that autumn felt absurdly long. At eight o'clock, well after the rest of America had drawn down its rattling shutter, a lush light stretched over our little watery patch of southern Florida. Our house, one of scores pitched along the ragged edge of the Everglades, sat in a small cul-de-sac that itself emptied by way of a connecting paved footpath into an even larger housing development, Elysium Gardens, which, with the exception of a single ghostly model house and several dozen concrete foundations, had never opened. Money trouble between the developer and bank, so the talk went. Black utility pipes bristled like decapitated daisy stems from the concrete foundations, across which the sand encroached in wavy layers, like cake icing, from old storm flooding, or just years of wind, doing its quiet work. Alligators occasionally nested in the sawgrass beside the footpath—you had to be careful to watch closely after young children and pets, the neighbors cautioned one another. Walking along with Sofia, I kept an eye trained on those placid-seeming thickets, ready to snatch her away. I'd warned her about snakes and black widows too, and so when she wanted to look under a particular rock, it was my job to flip the rock over.

"Those are just pill bugs," I said, pointing. They were scrambling for cover on legs as fine and delicate as eyelashes, one or two just lying there, dead. "We always called them roly-polies when I was a kid." I could see Sofia solemnly filing away this information, as if it might be useful down the road. "Don't worry, they don't bite," I told her.

"Unless I smack 'em. Then they'll sting me."

"Why would you want to smack them?" I remembered that kid Tony calmly kicking Tick's outstretched feet. "They can't sting. See, they're running away."

"That one isn't."

"He's just sleeping," I said.

We started home. "Oh, look!" Sofia shouted happily. A passenger jet was passing over us, the contrails from its wings converging in a shimmering golden line. If nothing else, Florida is garishly bighearted with its sunsets, and this one was certainly awe-inspiring, pink-clouded and apocalyptic. "I told you we'd have fun," Sofia said when our house appeared. Actually, she hadn't said that at all, but I nodded as if she had, and as we cut across the broom-stiff grass of our scorched backyard, I thanked her.

A week later when Tick came to my office for our Wednesday talk, I asked, "So what's up with you and Tony? You guys got friction?" A new bruise bulged like a little blue mushroom under his left eye.

"Man, that dude's nothing but friction."

"So what do we do about it?"

Tick's mouth tightened ironically. "You're a funny guy, Mr. Ross, you know that? *We.*" He seemed to want me to know that he forgave me, even if I occasionally asked stupid questions. Outside my office, where the Tonys of the world could kick you anytime the mood struck— to Tick, that was the real show, out *there.* This was just the intermission.

"All right. What do you feel like talking about?" I asked.

He wanted to talk about *Planet of Fear.* "It's about this robot, right? Only in the future, robots look like us. They got personalities. Like, you could be talking to one and not even know." I nodded, but I was already only half listening. Being told about a book's plot is a lot like enduring a long description of someone else's dream or illness, and I was becoming worn down by other people's illnesses and dreams. "This robot," Tick said, "he's like five hundred years old, like already middle-aged, and this other really old robot he works with, one day *he* starts talking about this planet. This perfect planet with no humans, way out on the edge of the galaxy. Old boy, they're fixing to cancel his ass any day now because he's about to hit a thousand years. That's like the magic number. You make it to a thousand, they cancel you." Tick's gaze, nervous at the best of times, kept flicking from my desk to my face, and I saw now that he had become aware of those whispering, frond-shaped shadows. "So old boy, he's like, 'We gotta get up outta here.'"

"You know," I said, "I think we need to figure out some way for you and Tony to get along. Before the situation gets out of hand."

"Look at my eye, man. Shit's already out of hand. From day one dude's been doggin' me. Anyway, you said you were gonna get me out of the stacks."

"I tried to."

Tick regarded me sadly.

"I did," I said. "I will."

"That room, man. It's crazy, Mr. Ross. People yelling all the time. Fights breaking out—over nonsense. You can't hear yourself think. Which ain't even the worst thing," Tick said. "I mean, the worst is when you're lying there at night, trying to sleep, and you just *know* you're about to get jumped. Like it's this weight." Tick laid a hand flat across his chest. "And you can't do a damn thing."

"Your face—did Tony do that to you?"

Tick shrugged.

"Come on, Tick. You gotta give me something."

Tick's eyes slid away cautiously. "I ain't no snitch." I could see the wall of ice fly up between us. *Snitches ain't nothin' but bitches*—you'd hear the younger kids chanting that in the hallways, reciting it like my daughter Sofia recited her alphabet. *Snitches get stitches.* "Look, I'm just *saying*, all right?" Tick said. "You gotta get me out of there. These thugs, they see some skinny little chump like me, it's like throwing meat to lions. Everybody splashing you with their radar, seeing if you're scared."

"Maybe they're scared too," I said.

Which was true, but how was that helpful? Everybody was frightened, and not just inside these walls. My father was terrified, yet he often appeared to be happily welcoming his own destruction, which in the end would come faster than any of us expected. Perched at his lectern, listening to me read, I could see him visibly relishing our little strolls through history's wreckage. The wails of grief rising like smoke over a dying world, the plague-sodden bodies left to rot in the streets, or tossed like garbage onto ships, and the ships cut adrift, burning.

A fiery falling star, a whiff of ashes on the air blown all the way from India, where, it was said, you could walk for weeks without hearing a single human voice. To my father, those plague ships, that star—a sign, the Florentines had decided, of God's ravening anger—were strangely comforting. It occurs to me now that if I had told him about Tick, as I sometimes felt inclined to, if I'd ever flung that in his face, my father would have simply taken it as further proof he'd been correct all along: that the hole steadily opening under Tick was the same hole yawning under him too, and all of us.

Afterward, I found Fuentes in his office. He was fiftyish, thick-waisted but strong as a bull from weight lifting, with a tidy little tanned head he kept razor-smooth. "Yeah, I saw your boy," he said. "So he got popped, big deal. These kids're always smacking each other, you know that." On the metal file cabinet behind his desk was a photo someone had taken of Fuentes, shirtless and grinning mightily, holding up a monstrous-looking, bloody fish in both hands.

"I just have a bad feeling about this one," I said.

Fuentes choked, laughing. "Goddamn, he's got you spooked, doesn't he?" But I wasn't going to leave empty-handed, and Fuentes saw that. "Fine, I'll have my guys give this Tony kid a shake, see what falls out," he said. "Can't move your boy right now. I'm jammed up already as it is."

"Just do what you can," I said.

At five, as I was packing up for the day, Fuentes' e-mail arrived. *Had Tony searched, as per our convr. Zilch on that. Kid's clean. Not even a toothpick. So much for your bad feeling. Tell your boy he needs to start standing up for himself. Oh and your welcome.* In my heart a weedy little flower unfolded itself and glowed at that lazy "your welcome." Which shows just what sort of pettiness I'm capable of, when push comes to shove.

Roaming among the sand-swept foundations of Elysium Gardens, Sofia said, "In Africa when you die they stick you in a hole sitting up and mash you down and throw dirt on you. Then everybody gets to walk on you. And nobody can come and cry after 'cause they don't know where you are."

"Who told you this?" I asked.

"Mrs. Martinson. She *lived* in Africa for a whole year. She says lots of people die there and you never know if you're walking on them or not, so you have to be careful."

Half a dozen airplanes crisscrossed the deep orange sky, their contrails dividing it into lonely tracts of real estate. "I'll be sad when you die," Sofia announced matter-of-factly. Perhaps that dead pill bug, the one I'd said was sleeping, was behind this declaration.

"So will I."

"Will you miss me?"

"Oh, terribly," I said. "Every day."

"I'll cry all the time, and I won't ever let anybody walk on you," Sofia said. "I'll read to you, like you do with Granddad." She bent down and rapped the sand with her fist, shouting, "Hello down there! Can you hear me?" Off in the sawgrass an alligator splashed heavily away, fleeing.

"I hear you."

Sofia giggled. "Very good," she said with mock primness, in what I could only assume was her best impression of Mrs. Martinson. "Now—what shall we read today?"

"You pick," I said.

In London, in that misty bygone era before I was born, my father had modeled himself after a once prominent Cromwell scholar whose star was even then fast fading, if my mother was to be believed. "Oh, he was such a fusty little snob—the professor, not your dad. Your dad was smitten. He'd never been around anyone like that before." *My father, smitten?* And why this particular professor, this moldy little nobody, and not Tuchman? Decades later my father still dressed with the same dowdy caution he'd first cultivated then, afraid of humiliating himself at afternoon tea. This from a man who had spent his earliest years mucking out stalls on a pig farm in Iowa, and who was now regularly driven over the high humming drawbridges of Miami by my chatty, cheerful, sundress-wearing mother to various neurologists, umbrella planted firmly upright between his knees, whatever the forecast. Occasionally, in order to give my mother a break, I would take him to his appointments. On this day, I remember—it would be the last time I drove my father anywhere—he was already fuming when I picked him up. Pulling into the clinic parking lot, he insisted I bring the pay ticket inside so I could get it validated and not have to pay the ten dollars, which he considered extortion. "All the mice must get their nibble before the bread's all gone," he said darkly. He'd reminded me about the ticket already, more than once.

In the waiting room, he surveyed the other patients, scowling. "My God, look at us. What's next—Lourdes?" In his herringbone coat and tie and heavy wool slacks, he could have been the indignant walk-on in some old BBC murder mystery, *Foyle's War* or *A Touch of Frost.* I intentionally steered him to a corner, but his voice, habitually tuned to the back of the classroom, was like a magnet, drawing attention in our wake.

"Lower your voice."

"Waving our little reliquaries," my father said. A white-haired woman in a blue-striped sailor blouse sitting nearby was gazing raptly into his face with a look of slow, hopeful recognition, while her companion—the bereft husband, I guessed—stared bleakly at the television across the room.

"I'll leave you here," I murmured.

"No, you won't," my father said. He smiled back at the white-haired woman, baring his teeth. Raising his voice again, he recited: "*E dure questo pistolenza fino a...*" It was a line I recognized from our latest romp through *A Distant Mirror,* the last words the great fourteenth-century historian Giovanni Villani was said to have penned, dying of plague at his writing desk in Florence: *In the midst of this pestilence there came to an end...*

When the receptionist called his name, my father straightened his tie, then stood. "I'll see you in a bit," I told him. The white-haired woman had lifted a trembling hand to her blouse, covering her heart. "Are you my Charlie?" she asked happily.

"No," my father said.

Crossing the JDC parking lot from my car, I spotted Fuentes, sitting alone on the old picnic table where the guards took their smoke breaks. An unlit cigarette lay cupped in his palm. He was staring down at it, as if he had no idea how the cigarette had gotten there. "I think you're supposed to light it," I said. Then I noticed the blood on his shoes.

Fuentes nodded grimly. "I keep trying to quit," he said. He looked up angrily, as if I'd laughed at him, and seeing my face, nodded again.

"Yeah, you probably don't want to go in there. They're still cleaning up." The sharp November sunlight drew a clean demarcation across the toes of his blood-smeared Nikes. Fuentes said, "I'd give anything to be out on my boat right now. Just me and the ocean. You fish?"

"No."

"Figures." He tossed the cigarette away, grimacing. "Hey, how 'bout that bad feeling of yours? What was that, you think? Somebody read your fortune?" He got up and went over to where the cigarette had fallen. When he lit it, inhaling hungrily, I saw how perfectly white and straight his teeth were. As a younger man he might have made a movie star, with those teeth.

"Whose blood is that?" I asked.

"Tony's," Fuentes said. "They got him over at Broward Memorial in surgery right now." He was smiling a little, in that tight, menacing way people sometimes smile when they're about to hit you. "Well, I guess if you're gonna snap, snap big. Your boy sure did." He blew smoke. "Don't even try pinning this mess on me."

"I wasn't going to."

"Just so we're straight," Fuentes said.

They had Tick in a processing cell. He was curled on the bench with his back to the door, as if asleep, but rolled over right away when the guard let me in. "I was wondering if I'd see you," he said, sitting up. A rime of dried soap was stuck to his earlobe. They'd made him shower in one of the delousing stalls—he'd gone straight back to his bunk after stabbing Tony, where a guard eventually found him, covered in blood. "They're saying I might get sent upstate as an adult. They can do that?"

"Yes," I said. Which they would, if Tony died.

Tick was quiet, absorbing this.

"Why, Tick?"

Tick shrugged miserably. "I just wanted it to stop." His thin chest heaved, as if the oxygen in the room had suddenly trickled away to nothing. "I almost didn't," he said. Standing over Tony, in the dark with the other boys asleep around them and everything for once, briefly, quiet and calm. "I guess somebody must've woke up and saw me," Tick said, blinking. "Because all of a sudden I hear some dude yelling, 'Do it!'" That one voice, Tick said, then a chorus of voices, screaming and roaring, a drumbeat, driving him on, and Tony, awake now, staring up at him, waiting as Tick had waited. Tick's face crumpled now, remembering. "You think maybe they'll let me bring my book with me? I was hoping I could read it again."

"I don't think so."

"But you could ask, right?"

"I'll ask," I said.

Tick wiped at his eyes. "That's where I got my name, you know." He had tried to tell me before, in my office, and even now wanted to—needed to, I understood now. "The humans, like they put these little bitty clocks inside the robots," Tick explained. "Only these clocks, they're counting *down*, right? Like a timer. From a thousand." He sighed deeply, as if he were suddenly tired, and lay back on the bench, looking up at the ceiling. "It's all right, you don't have to stay. I know you got stuff to do."

I shook my head. "Why the clocks?" I asked.

"Well, it's like, the humans, they're jealous," Tick said. "Because a robot, they break down, you just fix them. Long as you keep fixing them, they can pretty much live forever. The clock's just there to keep the humans happy." Tick shivered. The air conditioner had cycled on, a low rhythmic rumble in the ductwork. "So like anytime you want, if it's real quiet, you can just put your ear up close and hear that clock ticking down, and I guess you won't feel so lonely." Tick shut his eyes tightly now, as if he were listening. "Anyway, that's just the beginning of the book."

In the car days earlier, after his appointment, I'd asked my father what he thought your average medieval peasant, zapped by a time machine into the twenty-first century, might have made of our modern world. "Not much, I'd expect," he replied after a time. "I suppose once they got past the technological shock, they'd be fairly invisible." He had refused to discuss what the neurologist had told him, but from his mournful silence, I'd gathered the news wasn't good. We were passing over a drawbridge, the ribbed metal grating moaning under us, and he was looking down at the water below. "We like to think we've put all that dread and superstition behind us, but we haven't. Deep down, we're all still waiting for God to dump fire down on us." I was remembering this when the guard tapped lightly on the glass in the door to get my attention. I'd asked him to let me know if Tony's condition worsened. Here was my answer.

Tick said, "I could tell you the rest if you want."

"Please," I said.

MICHAEL KNIGHT
Jubilee

These two satisfied towns gaze at each other like old flames across Mobile Bay—handsome, hidebound Mobile with its lawyers and its cemeteries, and blithe Fairhope, pretty Fairhope, with its galleries and boutiques, Point Clear draped along the eastern shore like a string of pearls. Used to be, the right kind of Mobile family escaped to Fairhope in summer for the breezes, fleeing the humidity and mosquitoes and the bad air from the mills. The air is better now, but some of those families decided to stay—why shouldn't life be sweet as summer all year round?—enrolling their children in the little private school, wives fondling tomatoes at the farmers' market, husbands shuttling half an hour back across the bay during the week, that original migration in reverse, past the seafood dives and bait shops and the decommissioned battleship moored for tourists, to offices in downtown Mobile.

Such is the case with Dean and Kendra Walker. Here is Kendra in the kitchen, slicing hearts of palm while Dean prepares the grill out on the wharf. Friday, late September. The day's last light dissolving on the water. One has the impression that these long evenings will last forever, but already night is settling in by 7:30, and it's cool enough that Kendra will drape a cardigan over her shoulders when she goes out. While he waits for his wife to join him, Dean drinks single malt and pitches a tennis ball into the bay for their yellow lab, Popcorn, to retrieve.

From where she stands, Kendra can look out over the great room and through the windows along the porch. The lawn with its Bermuda grass and mossy live oaks. Then the boardwalk and the seawall and the beach, nearly covered at high tide. A row of wharves reaches into the bay, all those hammocks and Adirondack chairs, all those white boats suspended on their lifts. Across the water, a blazing sunset, that magnificent cliché.

The windows are open. Insects rattle in the grass. She scrapes the hearts of palm from the cutting board into a wooden bowl with black olives and endive. She'll wait to toss the salad until the steaks are nearly done. Her hands are bare, rings waiting on the sill. Their son, Thomas, named for Kendra's father, is back at school, a sophomore at the University of Alabama. The past month has been quiet. Kendra washes her hands, replaces her rings.

She's outside and across the boardwalk when Popcorn comes bounding down the wharf to greet her. He knows better than to jump on Kendra, so he hops and wags, careful not to make contact and she palms his back to settle him, his fur damp, his smell brackish. "Easy boy," she says and off he goes, paws thudding on the wood, to let Dean know that she's coming.

And here is Dean in weekend attire—worn polo, white shorts, brown loafers. His ankles are bare. His shins retain the faint patina of his summer tan. He will be fifty in November. Kendra has already picked out the invitations to his party. He does not look his age. He plays tennis twice a week. He has the posture of a military man, though her husband never served. He is taller than he appears. It's his eyes, she thinks. The gentleness in his eyes belies his height.

She takes her place at the wrought iron table. Dean fixes her a drink. They talk of nothing for a while—his day at work, hers at home— the conversation more rhythm than exchange of information. Music drifts over from the old hotel. Must be a band on the patio tonight. This silver bay is as familiar to Kendra as her husband's voice, but still a mystery, the only place in the world where shrimp and crab and flounder occasionally abandon deep water in the summer and swarm the shallows for no good reason, practically leaping into nets and buckets, presenting themselves for a feast. Jubilee, they call it, voices ringing along the shore. There was no jubilee this season, but nobody around here seems particularly concerned, least of all Dean and Kendra. They have the sunset and music from the old hotel. They have twenty-two years of marriage. They have good scotch and a good dog and not a cloud in sight.

Popcorn drops a waterlogged tennis ball at Dean's feet and he launches it as far as he can without rising from his chair. Before it hits the water, Popcorn is sprinting for the edge of the wharf, hurling his body elongate into the air. Even at high tide, it's a three-foot plunge, and watching the dog make his leap never fails to impress Kendra, the sheer unafraid athleticism of it. Once Popcorn retrieves the ball, he'll have to swim it all the way back to the beach, then run it all the way back out to the end of the wharf where he will drop it at her husband's feet again. Dean stands and wipes his right hand, his throwing hand, on the seat of his shorts.

"Well," he says, "let's light this fire."

In preparation for the moment, he has already stacked the charcoal and rinsed it with lighter fluid and rolled the grill out from under the tin roof. Popcorn returns with his tennis ball, so Dean chucks it one more time into the bay before striking a match and touching it to the coals, drawing his fingers back quickly to avoid the flame.

September flares out with a heat wave. There is work to be done around the house. There is always, it seems to Dean, work to be done. Sometimes he imagines that his wife begins redecorating in one corner and works her way month by month, room by room, until the whole house has been remade and she can begin again. He doesn't ask questions. He compliments the changes when he notices them. This house has been in his family for three generations but it is wholly Kendra's now.

Scaffolding goes up. Blue tarps. Trucks in the morning when Dean is leaving for work. Hammers and shouts. The housekeeper, Rosie, complains that workmen are always underfoot. Popcorn hides under the bed. Hispanic painters in spattered white, hardly more than boys, appear on the doorstep and ask if they might drink from the hose. Then, like shelling a shrimp, the scaffolding comes down, tarps are removed. Glistening, the Walkers' house emerges. One night, Dean pulls into the driveway and it is as if they have razed the original and constructed an exact replica in its place.

"Everything looks great," he tells his wife. "Just really great."

They are sipping scotch in heavy glasses, a fire in the hearth, though it's far too soon. Kendra drove past a farmer selling wood from the back of his truck. She was inspired. Dean thumbs the thermostat way down so they can enjoy it. On TV, the same old news. They will elect a president in November, less than a week before Dean's birthday.

"I was at the caterer's today."

"Hmmm."

Dean can feel himself drifting off.

"We'll have the tenderloin for sure," Kendra says. "And oysters, fried and raw. They're suggesting chicken too, but I was thinking catfish. Or tuna. Which would you prefer?"

"That sounds perfect."

She nudges him with her elbow.

"I asked you a question."

"I'm sorry," he says, rubbing his face. "Ask me again."

"Do you even care about this party?"

He can hear something close to exasperation in her voice, more emotion than the subject warrants, but he lets it be, figures it will smolder out on its own. Dean votes Republican without fail but he suspects that Kendra is leaning Democrat this year. Her ballot history is inconsistent. She voted for Clinton in '92, then against him after he cheated on his wife. She voted for Bush both times, then for Obama. Dean can't suss out the pattern but her private logic moves him. The fire twitches and sags. Popcorn sprawls before the flames until the heat becomes uncomfortable, then, sighing, retreats to the kitchen where the tile is always cool.

"Is that what you asked me before?" Dean rests his head on her shoulder. "I swear I heard something about catfish."

"Don't tease," she says. "I'm not in the mood."

Ten more minutes pass before Kendra feels his weight congeal against her, hears his breathing slow. She slips out from under him and he slumps sideways onto the couch. Popcorn rises with her. He shakes like he is wet. He looks at her with need in his eyes.

"All right," she says.

Outside, a full moon hidden by clouds, clouds and water tinted by its light like decorations at a dance. Kendra whistles and pats her hip, leading Popcorn up the boardwalk, his tail batting the air.

Hours later, Dean wakes up on the couch. The room is dark but for the remnants of the fire. Kendra has covered him with an afghan. For a moment, he doesn't know who or where he is. His heart is pounding. His entire life, his very substance, has been erased. Then he hears snoring—Popcorn dozing between the coffee table and the couch—and the world comes back. His heartbeat slows. The October night is still.

Kendra sleeps late on Saturdays, drawing slumber over her head like an extra blanket. Dean plays mixed doubles at the club. He will be home before noon, bearing bags of bread and cheese and cold cuts or shrimp to be boiled or takeout from Miss Lulu's. Bloody Mary mix if they're out. They will eat lunch, nap, then watch Alabama play football on TV.

Still drowsy, she carries the paper out to the porch, perusing the sports page for a question she might ask during the game. Dean takes such pleasure in explaining the minutiae. Popcorn keeps her company for a while, then pads over and stands belly deep in the bay, staring straight down into the water, his face serious, lost in concentration. He's only watching minnows. There was a time when Kendra was jealous of her husband's other women—that's how she thought of them—these short-haired, sturdy-thighed tennis ladies, these tan, midlife athletes, but her jealousy, like all unpleasant things, has faded. Kendra is no tennis player. She is a woman who knows how to set a table, how to make a guest feel welcome in her house, a woman who wears her beauty like an evening gown, her long limbs, her extravagant mouth. There is nothing sporty or offhand about her.

Popcorn stiffens in the water, ears cocked. Dean is home. Even before she hears his tires on the cockle shells, the dog is galloping around the house.

Half a minute later, her husband appears, screen door slapping shut behind him.

"I've got crabmeat. Fresh off the boat."

Kendra rakes her fingers through her hair. "I haven't even showered."

"This is how I like you best."

She can see Popcorn pressing his nose against the screen. "Is that a wet dog in my house?"

Dean's eyebrows jump up—surprised, guileless—above his sunglasses. He opens the screen door and Popcorn jangles out, prancing at Dean's knees, Dean thumping his sides.

"You old bad dog," he says. "You old wet dog. No wet dogs inside. You know better than that."

"So do you," Kendra says, displeased by the pettiness in her voice.

"How can I make it up to you?"

She leaves the sports page on the wicker table, pushes to her feet, kisses his cheek. "Let me take a shower," she says.

What had these mornings been like before her son went off to school, before he was born? She can't recall, not clearly. Instead a memory of hustling Thomas into church clothes leaps to mind, but that's tomorrow and she will have no little boy to cajole. While Dean cuts celery for Bloody Marys, Kendra prepares West Indies salad—lump crabmeat, chopped onions, olive oil, white vinegar. Their life revolves from meal to meal. They let their lunch chill for an hour, then eat it on Saltines.

"How did you play this morning?" Kendra says.

Her hair is still damp from the shower. She smells of coconut, roses. Dean's tongue darts out after a fleck of cracker on his cheek.

"My first serve was a little shaky but we won," he says. "Straight sets." Kendra clears the dishes. Dean loads them in the washer. They walk Popcorn without a leash. He trots along the water's edge, under other people's wharves, back up to the boardwalk to check in with Dean, the bay mud brown now and rough as bark.

At home, Dean brushes his teeth and strips to his boxer shorts, his chest paler than his face and forearms. They make love on cool, clean sheets. Lazy, inconsequential. This, too, a part of their routine. Kendra doesn't think she'll be able to sleep—she's not tired; her day has hardly started—but the Bloody Marys have sapped her strength and before long she is falling, falling, the buzz of an outboard motor fussing in through the screen.

The town of Fairhope was conceived as a kind of utopia, a place where a man might own what he created but the value of the land belonged to all. It was discussed in the journals of the day, visited by artists and intellectuals. Some hundred odd years later, Bay Street is all charming storefronts and cafés. There is art for sale, but it's priced beyond the reach of artists. If you didn't know better, you might assume that such a place was dreamed up by a woman like Kendra Walker. In her slacks and blouse. Her hair recently styled. You might assume that you know something about her. She sits in her car outside the salon and instructs a talent agent on her cell. She has booked a band for her husband's party. Dean likes Motown, beach music. He likes to dance. The band will set up in the ballroom of the old hotel. Her son is coming home. On her signal, Kendra tells the talent agent, the band should play "Happy Birthday," then follow it with that famous Otis Redding song. She imagines herself spinning on the dance floor, passed from Dean to Thomas, a rowdy horn section, backup singers, the night trembling with music and stars.

Rain mists on the windshield. Kendra cradles the phone in her lap. A mother emerges from the bookstore, trailed by two little girls. They are all wearing yellow raincoats and holding black umbrellas over their heads. The mother is carrying a shopping bag, heavy with new books. They proceed in a row, in order of age, tallest to shortest, one behind the other like ducks. Kendra puts the girls somewhere around ten and six, the mother in her middle thirties. School has just let out. Three doors down, they disappear into the bakery where, in another week, Kendra will place an order for her husband's cake. She dials Dean's direct line on her cell.

"Sweetheart," he says.

"I've got everything settled with the band."

Dean is sitting at his desk with his feet propped up. He didn't realize there was anything left to be settled. His office is in a brownstone on Conti Street, windows overlooking Cathedral Square. Rugs selected by his wife, photos of his son. The sign over the front door reads *Walker and Bolling, Attorneys at Law.* It's embellished with scales of justice designed to look like an anchor or an anchor that resembles scales of justice, depending on your perspective. They specialize in maritime cases, insurance claims relating to ships and cargo, civil matters between ship owners. Dean is almost never called upon to go to trial. They have three associates, four secretaries, two paralegals, and a runner who doubles as the IT guy.

"That's good news," he says.

The rain has already blown over on his side of the bay. On her side, the rain keeps sifting down.

"Everything else all right?" Dean says.

"Everything's fine. I just thought you'd like to know."

He drops his feet to the floor, drifts over to the window. The dome of the basilica rises above the oaks—beautiful, but Dean has always thought it looked mislaid, too eastern, not of this place. A homeless man dozes on a park bench in the square.

"Tell you what," he says, "why don't I take us out tonight? We haven't been to Felix's in a while. We'll have turtle soup."

"I don't like turtle soup."

"Of course not. You'll have the bisque."

"I do like bisque," she says.

Kendra can remember her first date with Dean as clearly as last night. It's the long stretch in between that's sometimes difficult to fathom. His friend Louis was married to her friend Mona, and Louis and Mona contrived to fix them up. You have so much in common, they said. Kendra was less than a year removed from Sweet Briar, working as a teller at a bank. Dean was one of forty associates at a big law firm. He had too much to drink at dinner. Kendra lost the keys to her apartment. Each apartment had a small wrought iron balcony and Dean proposed that he would climb up the outside of the building and let them in through the unlocked balcony doors.

"You're not serious," she said.

"I am indeed."

"You'll break your neck."

"It's not that high."

"But you're half drunk."

"When I'm half drunk," he said, "I'm twice the man."

It was at that moment, Kendra thinks, that she began to love him. He handed her his sport coat and commenced to climb, inching his way up the rain gutter, swinging his legs over the railing of the first balcony, then the next, like he had scaled at least one tall building every day of his life, that night leading inexplicably, inexorably to this night on the wharf, darkness hovering over the water like mist over a meadow.

Moths plink against the overhead, mesmerizing Popcorn. For a moment, he has forgotten the tennis ball lodged between his teeth.

"Thomas called," she says.

"Let me guess: he wants someone to write a check."

"He asked if he could bring a date to your party."

"White girl?" Dean says.

"You hush."

He laughs softly at his own bad joke. "What'd you tell him?"

"I told him I would speak to you."

"I think it's fine," Dean says. "What's this girl's name?"

And so on through the particulars of the phone call. The overhead bulb has a peculiar, insulating effect. Shadows stretch and lean in the oblong of its radiance, minnows flicking to the surface where light brushes the water. Beyond it, the bay is a pure dark slate. The universe ceases to exist.

Both of them acknowledge that Dean's party has gotten out of hand. They laugh about it over drinks. You add one name to the guest list and suddenly you've opened a door, crossed a border, and there are a dozen more you must include. In addition to organizing the party, Kendra has purchased a pair of antique cuff links, a shirt from Burke & Daniels, a box of monogrammed handkerchiefs. Dean folds them into the back pocket of his suits. Kendra appreciates the fact that her husband is so old-fashioned. He has an e-mail account for work but refuses to log on. His secretary's first job every morning is to survey his inbox, delete the clutter, print the ones that matter. The image of Dean at his desk reading printed e-mails swells Kendra's heart. He dictates his responses. His secretary clicks them off into the ether.

And this: He insists on Christmas stockings despite the fact that Thomas is too old. He likes to see them hanging heavy on the hearth. In Kendra's, he puts a hundred little things—bracelets and exotic liqueurs and vials of spices she will never use. Books filled with pithy inspiration. A watch in a velvet box. One-of-a-kind earrings. A wallet, a slender belt.

And this: Her husband is faithful. Of that Kendra has no doubt. He brings home the occasional rumor about his tennis buddies or men he knows from work, his voice thick with disappointment. Marriages pull apart around her. But not hers, never hers.

The alarm clock rouses Dean at 6:00 a.m. He shuts it off and rests there a moment on his back, adjusting to the light of a new day, his hand on his wife's warm hip. When the coffee is ready, he pours a cup and sips it in the driveway while Popcorn does his business, the sky hazy and gray. He showers, leaving enough hair in the drain to make him nervous, though he's not really going bald. Towel around his waist, Dean wipes steam from the mirror over the sink, his face always a slight surprise in the misted glass, not because he has forgotten how he looks but because his impression of himself never quite matches the image in the mirror. It's like hearing your own recorded voice, the sound familiar and strange at once. Somehow, the shaving cream on his cheeks makes his features recognizable again. Those are the same eyes that have been staring back at him from mirrors his whole life.

In his closet hang a dozen suits in dry-cleaning bags, his shoes lined up neatly on the floor. He dresses but waits to knot his tie. When Thomas was a boy, Dean would wake his son for school at this point in the ritual, his voice soft but firm, then drink a second cup of coffee on the wharf while Thomas performed his own ablutions. He gathered himself, became himself, in those moments, the view of the bay always the same. Thomas is gone, of course, but habit carries Dean out to the water, a pelican perched so still atop a channel marker it looks more decorative than alive.

This morning, however, this plain Tuesday morning, is different. Yes, Kendra will stir before too long to receive his goodbye kiss and, yes, a day of briefs and meetings awaits him at the office, but on this morning, Dean joins that dwindling portion of his fellow citizens who participate in the democratic process. He will cast his vote in the gymnasium of a middle school, the parking lot surrounded by campaign signs. The scene puts him in mind of a Polaroid as he steps out of his car, the colors a trace too bright. Two old white women with yellowing bouffants man the tables inside. Dean waits in line behind a black man in a wheelchair with a veteran's pin on the brim of his ball cap. In a few hours, Kendra will cancel out Dean's vote but it doesn't matter. He already suspects that his candidate will come up short. He'll win Alabama going away, but the swing state independents are breaking left, the resigned Midwest shedding its character at about the same rate that its industries are losing jobs. Even so, he goes through the motions, drawing the curtain aside, pressing the buttons. The old white women wish him well.

Duty done, he steers one-handed west across the bay, low tide exposing islands of mud and marsh grass, cars jostling for position, downtown Mobile revealing itself dead ahead. In five days, it will be official. Dean Walker will have lived for half a century.

Brooke Pitman is not the girl her son will marry. Kendra understands this right away. They arrive on the Friday afternoon before Dean's party, Thomas honking his horn in the driveway, stirring Popcorn to near mania. There is something vaguely foreign in the shape of her eyes. She's pretty but only that. Perhaps Kendra is being unfair. Some women don't come into substance until much later. Brooke, a year older than Thomas, spent the previous semester abroad. With one hand over her heart, she speaks of seeing *Titus Andronicus* at The Globe. But she is majoring in communications. She has a tattoo of a four-leaf clover on her ankle.

The house is immaculate. Rosie has been over everything with cloth and polish and feather duster. There are new sheets, washed and ironed, on the bed in the guest room. Thomas wants to show Brooke around. They stroll hand in hand along the boardwalk with Popcorn at their heels. To Kendra, Thomas looks self-conscious holding hands but he does not let her go. Kendra sets out pecans and grapes and olives so they will have something to snack on when they return. The lamps, the paintings. The burnished wood. Her house is rich in beautiful things, but none can compare to the view at this hour.

By the time Dean comes home from work, the three of them are drinking beer and playing Trivial Pursuit. Even drinking beer his wife is elegant. It's as if she is emitting light. She is almost frightening. The great room shimmers with her presence. She has a bottle in one hand, a game card in the other, slim bracelets dancing on her slim wrist. Thomas slouches easy at the table, Greek letters on his T-shirt. In an act of harmless sedition, he pledged ΣAE last year instead of ΔKE, his father's fraternity.

"This is Brooke," he says and the young woman stands, smoothes her skirt, presents her hand.

"Welcome," Dean says. "Let me fix a drink."

"Mrs. Walker is winning," Brooke says, meaning the game.

Her hand is warm and damp. Dean leaves his briefcase on a church pew by the door, kisses his wife, hugs his son, moves around the counter to the kitchen, Popcorn nosing the back of his knee.

"Speaking of which," Kendra says, "what did Portuguese explorers christen *O Rio Mar* in the sixteenth century?"

"Don't answer," Thomas says. "This is for a pie piece."

"She's killing us," Brooke says.

The ice, the whiskey. That first sip.

"The Amazon," Dean says.

Thomas and Brooke groan. Dean lets Popcorn lick an ice cube from his palm. The scene before him fills him up. It's not contentment exactly and it's not pride, though those things are mixed in with what he feels. His son needs a haircut but he's found himself a girl. Maybe she likes it long. Thomas has his mother's hair, straight and blond and glossy. Dean takes his place at the table beside his wife, slips his arm around her back.

"You're on my team," Kendra says.

Later, in bed, Dean holds a biography of Abraham Lincoln open on his lap, reading glasses perched on the end of his nose. All that whiskey has made it difficult to focus. Kendra is amending herself with creams and lotions, the bathroom door ajar.

"Well," he asks her, "what do you think?"

"Keep your voice down."

Thomas and Brooke are watching a movie in the great room.

"They can't hear us."

"Just in case," she says.

"I like her."

"She seems nice."

"She's very pretty."

"I suppose."

Kendra emerges in silk pajamas and sits on the edge of the mattress, her back to Dean, her hair drawn over her right shoulder to be brushed, the rim of her left ear exposed.

"They're not in love," she says.

Later still, Kendra hears her son's door creaking open, his footsteps in the hall, their voices hushed and playful. She scoots closer to Dean, rests her head on his chest. His chest rises and falls. She holds him tight as the world goes spinning off beneath their bed.

This old hotel was built in 1847, forty rooms and a restaurant on the tip of Point Clear, the very place a pendant would dangle from a chain. Seventeen years later, the Confederates commandeered it for a hospital, their gravestones still visible from the 18th tee. The golf course was added in the twenties, more rooms, swanky cottages, the grand ballroom. It's said that F. Scott Fitzgerald was a guest in the new wing, though no photos of his stay exist. The Army Air Corps used the hotel as a training base during WWII, those polite boys removing their boots before entering to preserve the hardwood floors, that history shining like wax on every surface, in every room and hall, on the brass-railed bar, windows reflecting wavery images of passing figures, walking paths buckled by the roots of oak trees even older than the hotel.

At the first hint of evening, lights flicker on inside and out, drawing the hotel out of the gloom, making it glimmer and shine, a great ship, an ocean liner from another time about to embark upon a long voyage across a wide and tranquil sea. Kendra has already made several trips back and forth from house to ballroom checking in with the event staff, the caterer, the band. Everything proceeds apace. It will be Thanksgiving in two weeks. In her slip, blow-drying her hair, it occurs to Kendra that her wedding was only slightly more elaborate. But the party was Dean's idea. She asked him what he wanted for his birthday and he said food and friends and music, plenty to drink. She'd been thinking of a trip— Rome or Paris, just the two of them. When she emerges from the bathroom, hair warm against her neck, there is Dean humming as he fingers studs into his tuxedo shirt, and her reservations fall away. This party is not a black-tie affair. The other men will be wearing blazers and slacks, shirts open at the collar. Dean pretends he's sporting his tux ironically, but Kendra knows he likes the way it looks.

"I don't want there to be any question," he says, "just who's the man of honor at this shindig."

With Thomas and Brooke, they open Dean's presents and drink champagne in the great room, a private moment before the party. Dean makes a fuss over his gifts. Even Brooke has brought him something, an Alabama jersey with the number 50 on both sides, purchased at the campus bookstore.

"It's nothing," Brooke says. "A token."

Her modesty is becoming. Her calves are taut in her high heels. Her youth makes Kendra's heart race. Thomas beams, already on his third glass.

Then, finally, it's time to go. Night has fallen. Kendra sends Thomas and Brooke on ahead to greet the early arrivals, headlights even now brushing back the darkness. The valets will have their hands full. More people are coming than Kendra could have guessed. Her husband is that esteemed. His partner, Arthur Bolling, will be present, along with all three of their associates. There will be clients, like Walter Willett, who runs a tugboat operation, and A. B. Random, who owns a shipbuilding concern. His wife, Muriel, is one of Kendra's favorites, a perfect Mobile lady. Erik Nooteboom, whose company transports materials all over the world, is winging in from Denmark. Dean provides counsel for his activities in the Gulf. There will be old friends like Diane and Curtis Henley and Jeb and Posey White and Dean's tennis buddy, Paul St. Clair, who left his wife in June. Martha and Buddy Bragg accepted the invitation. Their son, Henry, is a fraternity brother of Thomas' at Alabama. Louis and Mona, who finagled Kendra's first date with her husband, will be attending, though they are long divorced. Mona will be unescorted. Louis is bringing his third wife. On and on, the guest list goes—Isaac and Trina Yates, Ellen and Charlie Caldwell, Marcus

Weems, who lost his wife to cancer—names mapping the itinerary of their marriage.

Popcorn shimmies and whines, nuzzling their limp fingers, their clothes. He is aware that something out of the ordinary is afoot. He is right to suspect that he will be left out. "Sorry boy," Dean says, easing the door closed, the dog mashing his wet nose against the glass.

Arm in arm, Dean and Kendra make their way along the boardwalk. Their house is only six driveways from the old hotel. The night is crisp enough to mist their breath, moonlight glinting on the bay like broken glass.

"You look beautiful," Dean says, and Kendra says, "So do you."

They pass beneath the oaks, branches draped with moss. Suddenly, Dean is nervous. It's like the dream in which he enters a courtroom unprepared. He has made a mistake. His tuxedo is absurd. He has no idea what he will say to his guests. There is nothing important left to talk about. A dozen bicycles lean in a rack, waiting for hotel guests to claim them. The flag is lifeless on its pole. There is no wind, no chatter of insects.

At last, the famous ballroom emerges from the night, all delicate light and lofty windows, guests already mingling beyond the glass, waiters passing hors d'oeuvres. The voices from inside reach them muted and obscure, another frame sliding forward in Dean's dream, the one where everyone is speaking a language he cannot understand.

"Wait," Kendra says, tugging his arm.

"What is it?"

"Just look," she says. "They're here for you."

All those familiar faces. It's like gazing into the past. Elbow to elbow at the bar, Buddy Bragg and Charlie Caldwell and Isaac Yates wait for their drinks, their wives standing to one side. Paul St. Clair is talking Alabama football with Marcus Weems. There is only one subject in the fall that could make their faces so intent. Behind them, Thomas and Brooke are laughing at something A. B. Random has just said. Decorous Muriel swats her husband's bicep. The joke must have been unseemly. Thomas' teeth flash when he laughs, the crooked incisors of his childhood straightened long ago.

And here are Dean and Kendra Walker alone together in the dark. She kisses his jaw, wipes the lipstick print with the heel of her hand. His rush of nerves is passing. He just needs a drink, that's all. On their wedding day, Dean persuaded a bridesmaid to slip Kendra a note. *It's not too late. We can still elope.* Kendra held onto it for years. She kept it in a box with tarnished hinges, along with other personal souvenirs—a matchbook, a mateless earring, a ticket stub. Now it is too late. It's far too late. Faintly, from back the way they've come, they can hear Popcorn barking, the sound of him shrill and broken-hearted. They must stay this course until the end.

JO LLOYD
The Ground the Deck

When Megan first moved to London, she lived in the top of a house at the top of Brixton Hill that seemed to her, all fresh and green and hopeful as she was, the very best place in the city. She had been staying in a thieves' hostel near Victoria while she was looking for somewhere to live, eating biscuits and sleeping in her clothes, and the first six flatshares she'd been to see didn't want her, so she was grateful beyond words when Licia and Xander said they'd love to have her live with them, they were kindred spirits, she could move in just as soon as she liked, that very day if she wanted.

Right now in fact, Licia said. Go and fetch your things. I cannot *bear* another minute cooped up here with no one but Xander.

Xander inclined his head slowly toward Megan. I am inured to her insults, he said.

Megan thought of the underground, in which she had got lost twice already, and the two lumpy unmanageable body bags that held everything she had thought she would need in the world. It might take me a couple of trips, she said.

Xander will go with you, Licia said.

Because I have nothing better to do than run around at her whim, said Xander.

It'll be good for him. He hasn't opened the front door in days.

I'll have you know, darling—

But Licia interrupted him. You should get a taxi.

A taxi, Megan said. How much would that cost?

In fact, let's all go. It'll be fun.

And that was what they did. They took the tube to Victoria and Megan repacked the few items she had dared to unpack while Licia and Xander waited, scrutinizing the narrow bed and the sticky floor but paying no attention to the No Smoking signs. Downstairs, at some invisible, practiced gesture from Licia, a taxi appeared, and they rode through the snarled traffic at a processional crawl, as if to allow their subjects the opportunity to wave.

The flat was in a redbrick terrace near the prison and was perfectly adequate for two people, which was the number on the lease. With three squeezed in, it became almost affordable, but only by caring for money more than it deserved. If Megan had been stopped in the street at this time and quizzed on the subject, she could have told the name and age of every coin in her purse. But this was just a rough patch, she knew. They would beat through it to the lives they were supposed to live, where they would subsist on air and art and sunlight.

Licia was working in a gallery, a position too sought-after to require adequate payment, and taking classes in life drawing and photography and printmaking until she could decide in which medium exactly her talents lay. The flat would often be obstructed for days by some piece that was struggling to meet her standards. Megan had one of her half-finished oils in her room, a woman looking out suspiciously, or perhaps eagerly, from a patch of murky blue. She had told Licia she liked it as it was. Take it, Licia said. It's hideous. It's doomed. I never want to see it again.

Xander was signing on and working at what he always referred to as his first novel. He admired writers like Lowry and Hemingway, who drank enormous amounts and produced their novels effortlessly in their sleep, and was doing his best to emulate them. The novel was forever stopping and starting, the plot reversing, the characters changing age and century and gender. But any day now, they were all confident, it would come flowing out, fully formed.

Megan had found a temporary data entry job because she could type very fast and people would pay you to do that, although not quite enough to live on. What she wanted to do was work in television or film or magazines, something with a clear story told in pictures. Her idea of what this would entail was hazy. She saw herself progressing to a position of authority where the pictures would be at her disposal, together with minions, who at the flick of her finger would rearrange them as she chose. She pursued this vision of her future mainly by sending out begging letters. Dear Sir or Madam, Please employ me. I have German and Art History, I can ride a unicycle and once organized a charity fashion show, I am full of talent and creativity, ask anyone. Occasionally, they would write back to express regret or pity, which she took as proof that her strategy would succeed. In the meantime, she got up cruelly early every day to take a bus and two tubes so that she could spend seven and a half hours keying in requisition orders for the multitude of small and large pieces on which a railway depends for its continued smooth running.

The downstairs flat had the garden and their flat had the balcony overlooking the garden. All winter it meant nothing to them. They put a blanket over the window to keep the heat in; they might as well have lived in a cave. But as soon as the weather turned warm, they took the blanket down and opened the window wide. There was just enough room on the balcony for three kitchen chairs, and they would sit in a row, their knees pressed against the railings, looking out over the top of the prison and the backs of houses, the gardens and sheds and blocks of flats stretching down the hill to where the riots had been. Licia and Xander liked to imagine what they would do if there were riots again, how they would listen to the sirens, watch the fires burn, the smoke hanging in the sky like a dirty fog. But there were no riots, and no wars either. Or if there were wars, they were so contained and far away it was hard to be sure if they were wars or something else. There was no blackout, no rationing, no conscription. No one required them to participate or even protest. Gradually, the colors would fade and lights would start to come on here and there. The air smelled of petrol and dust, that small London dust that was invisible and sharp as glass and forever insinuating its way into clothes. There would be traffic noise from the hill, and fragments of conversation from the street in front, and always a blackbird sobbing out its song from the heart of a lilac. As the evening cooled, they would fetch the blanket that had hung over the window and settle it around their knees. The buildings and gardens would sink into a pool of darkness that deepened and spread as the lights glowed brighter, and they would look out over it all, like passengers on an ocean liner, watching over the bow rails as the dreaming blue land of their future rose on the horizon, hurrying nearer with every moment, its lights winking hope and promise.

A few weeks after Megan moved in, Licia took her to lunch with an elderly aunt and uncle. Megan was invited, she supposed, only because Xander was engaged elsewhere, although what excuse would have withstood the force of Licia's will she couldn't imagine. Before they went into the restaurant, Licia listed suitable and unsuitable topics of conversation for her. The waiters spoke in French, and everyone except Megan replied in French. The aunt and uncle told stories about palaces in Venice and villas in Paris, penthouse apartments overlooking Central Park where a new pane of glass had to be winched up the side of the building, inch by inch. With no home of their own, they toured from one of these places to the next, staying for weeks, months, in spacious chambers where an extra guest or two would hardly show. Aunt Bea had a calm round face, untouched by the age that had crumpled her body, and seemed to Megan at peace with the world. Afterward she said this to Licia, who exclaimed at her naïveté.

She's the most frightful snob, Licia said. And she bosses Uncle Teddy around, you have no idea.

Really?

She was dirt poor before she met him. I mean *dirt* poor. And since she got hold of the purse strings, she hasn't allowed him the least say. Not the *least*.

Licia herself did not believe in restricting her lifestyle to her earnings, and was in the happy position of not having to. Her parents (The Parents, she called them, as if they were the only ones in the world) were forever buying her extravagant gifts and sending her hampers from Fortnum and Mason. Every spring and autumn, she and her mother went out to buy Licia a new summer wardrobe and a new winter wardrobe. If Licia were to peer from the top of a tall staircase, or teeter along a perilous rooftop, she would see The Parents waiting below, with mattresses spread out to catch her, duvets and goose down pillows. The feathers buoyed her steps; her feet, in their Italian leather shoes, never quite made contact with the pavement. She was always the one turning up the heat or throwing out two-day-old bread or buying white rum and vermouth to make cocktails.

Xander came from a rich family too, but he had fallen out with them, possibly over the writer thing, or maybe the gay thing; anyway, he didn't see them at all, except sometimes an aspiring-politician brother he despised. Oh darling, he said when Megan asked him about the brother. He's exactly the kind of grunting truffle-grubbing breeder you would expect. And so is his wife and that dreadful piglet child.

Xander considered himself independent, and was proud of it. His only responsibility was to go down to the dole office every Wednesday to confirm that he was alive and actively looking for work. He answered these questions without embarrassment, and probably they heard his answers without surprise. It was enough finding jobs for the yearning masses who came in every day banging their fists on the counter and weeping, without having to worry about Xander. Every so often, for the sake of form perhaps, they sent him on an interview. He made not the slightest effort to appear anything other than he was—turning up in his red silk slash-front shirt with his hair tumbling across his eyes, folding his long limbs into martyred poses, calling the interviewer darling—and no one had yet shown any interest in employing him in even the most menial position.

As for Megan, she didn't have much family, and what there was had nothing of anything at all. She had never known her father, a sailor who'd come ashore just long enough to whirl her mother round the Palais and leave her with the name of his ship on the back of a cigarette packet. Years later, when Megan tried to track him down, she found out it was not, in fact, a ship, but a signaling base in the middle of the country. The Navy, she discovered, names all its establishments as if they are ships, and acts as if they are at sea, so her father would have said port and starboard, and taken shore leave, and called the ground the deck, even if he never felt it roll beneath him.

Megan's grandparents threw her mother out when they learned she was pregnant. But a couple of years later, when Megan's grandmother died, Grandad Charlie relented and let her move back in. Mostly so that she could take care of him and Megan's Auntie Dot, who couldn't read or write, and needed a lot of taking care of.

Shortly before Megan moved to London, Grandad Charlie died unexpectedly, and there was no money to pay for the funeral. Charlie might have been an old curmudgeon who hadn't been very kind to Megan's mother or her grandmother, or to anyone actually, but he still needed, deserved even, a send-off. Megan's mother was so distressed by it she became altogether helpless. I don't know what to do, she kept saying. What will people think? Auntie Dot came to the rescue, for surely the first and only time in her life, by remembering Harry the Insurance Man. Harry used to come round every Friday when Megan was small, collecting the mite that people set aside for death and disaster. He often used to stop and have a cup of tea with them. They were his favorite customers, he always said. How are my favorite customers today? The insurance company didn't know anything about Harry. They were interested only in the papers that Grandad Charlie, who'd got paranoid in his last years, had shredded or burned or eaten. Megan spent two whole days on the phone, and finally they paid up. It was nothing, the merest pittance, but it did buy a coffin and enough flowers piled on top of it to let her mother look the neighbors in the eye.

Megan swore that she was never going to find herself in that situation again. A few weeks later, on a day slippery with gray snow, she got on a coach and waved goodbye to her mother and Auntie Dot. Through the salt-grimed windows, they were already hard to distinguish from the other aunts and mothers, leaning in the cold, hugging their coats tight. She smiled at them and let herself believe that they were smiling back. She knew she was doing the right thing. She was going to a place where nobody sat waiting for death and disaster, a place where people lived rich cultural lives, went to the opera and the ballet and the theater, discussed the important matters of the day, and, when the walls of inequality and injustice towered too high, got together to break them down.

She did not, of course, expect all this to be laid at her feet the moment she arrived.

Every day, she got up in the dark and pulled on socks and coat to go to the bathroom, often passing a sleeping Xander on the way. Megan's name was not on the lease, but because she was paying rent, she had her own room, while Xander usually shared with Licia. But Licia would bring home some studded youth she'd found in the street, or she and Xander would squabble, and then Xander would end up on the couch, bundled up in the icy predawn, perfectly still, like one of those bundles Megan would see an hour later when she came up out of the tube, a bundle of clothes in a doorway, wrapped up so tight it was hard to tell which end was which or whether the person inside was alive or dead, and she would count her blessings, burrowing her face down into her coat, although less than a minute later she would forget she was blessed, as she pushed through biting wind and crowds to reach an old-fashioned office block where a middle-aged woman called Eunice, who wore a wig and dressed like the Queen, had power of life and death over Megan and the other data entry staff.

Megan was very good at this monotonous, ridiculous job. She raced through her requisition forms with hardly an error. Because of this,

Eunice, who was a tyrant, returning work arbitrarily, indulging her favorites and bullying everyone else, started to show her a grudging respect. I will say this, she said, looking over her glasses as if she'd spotted a talking monkey, you are careful in your work (*caiirful*, she pronounced it, with her St. Kitts accent). Once or twice there was a condolence letter to do, when an employee had been killed on the railway, and Eunice assigned these to Megan. She felt a touch of pride in this small distinction, although she felt nothing at all about the man who had died or the widow she was writing to.

At the end of the day, she pushed back down into the underground, where the wind was funneled into a weapon directed, like a water cannon, at the masses shuffling forward. At Brixton, the crowds battled to get out of the station. There would be policemen at the entrance, trying to look cheerful and approachable, the riots were in the past, everyone was on the same side now. But the younger ones were jumpy, touching their conspicuous hats for reassurance as the currents surged around them. Outside, the queues for the bus were ten thick, people shoved and wrestled, knocked one another to the floor. Megan would pick herself up, brush herself off, wait for the next bus.

What she dreamed of, what she craved, on the bus, on the tube, standing in queues for the bus and the tube, was sleep. She used to imagine that if she had a lot of money, she would buy art and a space to hang it, vast windows through which light would pour to reveal truth and beauty. Now it seemed to her what anyone would buy was sleep. That would be the first thing. After that, food and clothes and swimming pools. Then you'd put a big lilo in your swimming pool and sleep there too.

On the weekend, she wouldn't move until eleven or twelve or whatever time Licia's latest went out the door and Licia came past her room crying, What was I thinking? Whatever was I thinking? Which was what she said about all of them except for that brief period when she'd been in love with Benjamin the alcoholic architect. But that had ended badly. When Megan went through, Xander would be sitting on the couch, his duvet wrapped around him and his foppish hair, not so foppish in the morning, sprouting over the top of it, a little cloud of smoke above his head. They'd make tea and toast, turn on the radio, and sit there in their cave. After a while, Megan would fetch the paper from the hall and they would go through it picking out jobs for which she was totally unqualified. You have to start at the top, Licia would say, when Megan protested.

She didn't go to the opera or the ballet or the theater, because she couldn't afford it. She went sometimes to museums, those that were free, and to openings at Licia's gallery, which were also free and where there was wine. Occasionally, they went down to the Ritzy or the Academy, or up to the South Bank or Camden. But mostly they just hung out, dissecting Licia's young men, mocking people they worked with, or laughing about Licia's mother's charity lunches, Xander's father's model soldiers, everything they had escaped.

And so in this way the winter passed, long months of it, each one much the same as the last. Xander had rewritten the first page of his novel thirty times. Licia had abandoned equal numbers of men and works of art. And Megan was still, for the moment, at the railway.

Toward the end of that winter, three things happened that seemed to Megan later to have been related with a significance she didn't note at the time.

Firstly, she was offered a job, not the job she had applied for but a more lowly position. Much more lowly, an assistant to the assistant absolute nobody, as Licia said. The salary was less even than Megan was making at the railway. And look, said Licia, it's not even in London. You'd have to move out to some frightful soulless suburb. You don't want to leave us, do you? After much agonizing, Megan decided not to accept it. There would be other, better jobs, as Licia said. The very thing you wanted, in her experience, always came along sooner or later.

Secondly, new tenants moved into the downstairs flat. They seemed too young to be married, barely schoolchildren, but that's what it said on their post, Mr. and Mrs. Unwin, Mrs. C. Unwin. They both worked for the Inland Revenue, Xander reported, or some other dull and unsavory branch of the civil service. They were small and frail, and clung to each other when they walked down the street, like refugees in a storm.

Notes began to appear, slid under the door of the flat early in the morning or late at night. To Our Upstairs Neighbors, they began, and were signed Your Downstairs Neighbors. In between, there would be a reasonably worded plea for the better management of their shared space. Pick the post up off the hall floor. Don't overfill the bins. Then a cheerleading exclamation mark. Better for us all! We hope you agree! In all the years Licia and Xander had been in the flat they had hardly registered that people lived downstairs. Can you believe their cheek? they said. Who are they anyway? They made fun of the Unwins' cheap clothes and regular hours, as if poverty and a steady job were peculiar to them. They piled the bins higher, left the milk bottles rolling in the path, walked right over the post. The unseen hands of the Unwins continued to make their appeals. The exclamation marks doubled, tripled. Then the notes stopped. The Unwins receded into the shadows beyond the hall where nobody was required to think of them.

The third thing was that Xander fell madly, utterly, overwhelmingly in love with a playwright/plasterer he met in the dole queue, and disappeared for several weeks. In his absence, Licia took Megan to some private views. She put her arm through Megan's and introduced her to sleek, bright bird-people as My good friend, Megan. They cooked dinner together, pasta or baked potatoes. They curled up on the couch, and Licia told Megan how much she envied her hair and what she should do with it. She pointed out how her own hair had been cut to divert attention from her worst features (she particularly disliked her nose), a style it had taken most of her life and an outrageously expensive hairdresser to discover and to which she would now be faithful. They sat up late drinking Licia's vodka until they were full of hope and nostalgia. Megan told Licia about her hazy dreams, the pictures and the minions. She told her about her mother and her Auntie Dot and the mistake (Megan) that had set the course of her mother's life. If either of them got ill or died, she would have to, she had always thought at least, that she would surely go back and look after the other one. (Madness! said Licia. Suicide!) She told Licia about her sailor father, roving, as she then believed, across the steep rolling seas. Which was not something she told everybody. Licia told Megan about every boyfriend she'd had since the age of twelve, every one a fool and not one of them able to make her believe for a moment that she was any better than she was. This was, she said, why she had liked Benjamin the alcoholic architect, who was straight-talking and had never tried to flatter her. He had seen through her from the start, and for this reason, she had felt safe with him. Although, as it turned out, she had not been.

When Xander returned, forlorn and rejected and minus his meager savings, which he had either spent on or given to the plasterer playwright in a fruitless attempt to hold on to his affections, Licia gathered him in and set about comforting him, exactly as, it turned out, she had done all the other times this had happened. Suddenly, Licia and Xander were whispering in corners, exchanging meaningful looks, changing the subject when Megan entered the room. Xander looked thinner than ever, his hair drooped, his eyes were red and bruised. But in Megan's hearing, anything he said about the affair was upbeat, ironic. Licia, in Megan's hearing, never mentioned it.

Gradually, Xander returned to his old self. His hair regained its bounce, he and Licia began bickering again, and the three of them went back to hanging out together. By then the season had changed.

There was no spring that year. No scent of cut grass, no blossom, no softening breeze flicking playfully at knees and curtains. All at once it was hot and oppressive. The leaves on the trees came out and immediately blackened and dropped. The flowers withered. Even the weeds that chanced their luck in the cracks between pavement and houses shriveled. In the park by the flat, there was nothing but dust and gravel. The children flung themselves down on the gravel and cried, the teenagers threw cigarettes, the lovers quarreled, the dogs fought.

Their small balcony was a gateway cut into the dome of heat. They passed through it into the evening air, looking out in pity at the rest of London lying flat and defeated below them. They drank muddy brown cocktails improvised with Licia's blender and fruit sold off cheap at the market, and congratulated themselves on their wisdom.

We could be making car parts, said Licia. Or selling ad space.

Or working in the plastic bucket factory, said Megan, who had done this for a month one summer.

Or worse, drawled Xander. We could be in stocks and shares.

Licia frowned at Xander. Anyway, she said. We're very wise.

Although actually, said Megan, I hate my job.

You'll find something, said Licia. I mean how long have you been here? No time at *all!*

I suppose so, said Megan. Although that was less true this week than it had been last. She had had to borrow this month's rent from Licia. And on the inside of her smart—her only—jacket, she had found a hard, flaking gray spot where some person on the bus had, for who knows what reason, quietly reached inside and pressed chewing gum into the lining.

Then Licia surprised Megan by asking what she wanted to do for her birthday in a week's time.

I'm going home.

No no *no!* said Licia. It's your first birthday with us.

They'll have made a cake.

We can make a cake.

Xander rolled his eyes. We can buy a cake, he said.

Megan knew her mother would have already got her a present, a blouse, say, that she would have saved up for and that Megan would never wear, and she would have helped Auntie Dot buy some trinket, and written a card for her. They would watch her unwrap these presents and her mother would say, Is it all right, hen? You can take it back if you want. Are you sure it's all right? I kept the receipt. And then they would ask about her job, which they thought a miracle of loaves and fishes, neither of them having the faintest idea how anybody went about getting a job. It would be warm in the flat, but they wouldn't open the windows. They had a horror of catching a chill.

You absolutely *must* stay here, said Licia. And you must have a party.

I don't know anyone to have a party for.

Of course you do. There's that cousin of yours, Yvette.

Yvette was some kind of step-relation whose details Megan's mother had insisted on looking up when Megan moved to London. They had met up a couple of times early on. Yvette wore wide print skirts and what looked like pearls. She was proud that she had mostly lost her accent, and asked Megan how long she thought she would keep hers. She talked a lot about her work, which Megan was given to understand was very demanding, and particularly about her boss, how he joked about seeing more of Yvette than his wife, how he was building a dovecot in his garden for his daughter's wedding.

I don't think so, said Megan.

Then there's Isaac, Licia continued.

Xander made a noise that indicated derision.

Megan had met Isaac at Licia's gallery. She had been struck by his eyes and the large hole in his jumper, which she took to be daring rather than slovenly, and how he studied each picture at length before forming an implacable judgment. Isaac was a poet and held strong opinions on a range of subjects. He particularly admired Henry Miller and carried *Tropic of Cancer* like a large medal pinned to his chest. Licia and Xander sniggered at him and made fun of his poetry, so Megan stopped taking him to the flat. Instead, they went to his bedsit in Vauxhall, where there was one glass and one plate and he recited passages out of books she had failed to read and criticized her underwear.

I don't actually see him anymore, she said.

And I'll invite those people from downstairs, said Licia.

Xander groaned. Oh, darling, no. They're such hicks. I swear they must be Appalachian.

Appalachian pinheads, said Licia.

They're probably brother and sister, said Xander.

Incestuous Appalachian pinheads.

Xander and Licia could keep this up for some time. Even if I were having a party, Megan said, I wouldn't invite them.

And there's my college friends, said Licia. I can bring a whole crowd.

Licia's college friends were freakishly tall and wore sparkly clothes and told the same anecdotes over and over.

Nor them, Megan said.

Xander leaned toward Megan as if to whisper, but he didn't whisper. You know why she wants a party, he said. She wants to invite her new man.

What new man?

Her mother introduced them. He has a house in Chelsea and a Jag. Ask her what he does.

Xander knows perfectly well what he does, said Licia.

She's afraid to say it aloud.

He works in the City.

He's a stockbroker! said Xander. They despised stockbrokers. Also bankers, lawyers, estate agents. Anyone who made money.

Si's passionate about art, said Licia. He bought a painting from me.

He's not *passionate*, darling. He invests in it. It's all gilt-edged bonds to him.

Xander's jealous, said Licia. Si's charming. And witty. And there's absolutely nothing wrong with having a house in Chelsea.

So will we be meeting him? Xander persisted.

Anyway, you don't know him, said Licia. It would be a little odd for you to invite him to your party.

I'm not having a party, Megan reminded her.

She finally managed to persuade Licia that there would be no party. But she did agree to stay and spend her birthday with Licia and Xander. Your best friends, as Licia said. Licia would cook dinner (Xander rolled his eyes again) and they would have a fabulous time.

Licia told Megan dinner would be at eight and she was not to come any earlier. After work, she walked round a park near the office. It was hotter than ever and she could feel the ruts in the path through her impractical thin sandals. She went to a museum that was open late. She was the only person there, slapping through corridors of pouty dukes and duchesses like some stranded sea creature.

On the way to the tube she rang home. Did you get the parcel? her mother asked immediately. She had never trusted the post office, or anything else that claimed to traverse the country purposefully to arrive at a known destination. I still have the receipt, she said. Then, as an afterthought, Happy birthday. She asked how Megan was spending her day, and Megan said she'd been at work. Really? her mother said. That's wonderful. Megan said Licia was going to bake a cake, and her mother said Really, hen? Well, that's wonderful. Then she put Auntie Dot on and Megan had to go through it again, the post, work, the cake.

As she approached the flat, she could hear noise, and she knew, sinkingly, what it would be. She realized she had known all along.

All the people she'd said she didn't want to see were there. Yvette, Isaac, the Unwins. Also seven or eight of Licia's tallest and sparkliest friends, a junkie friend of Xander's who'd once told her she had the hands of a washerwoman, and Benjamin the alcoholic architect, whose name she had been forbidden to mention on pain of death.

Licia came hurrying up. Meggy Peg, you're here. Happy birthday. Isn't this fabulous?

We said dinner.

But this is better. Come and have a drink.

She let Licia pour her wine and tell her what fun it was and pour more wine and tell her how she'd happened to bump into Benjamin and pour more wine until slowly gravity started to lose its hold. Xander drifted over and wished Megan happy birthday and hissed in Licia's ear before drifting away. They were quarreling again, Megan thought. She started to think how nice it was of Licia to do this, even though she had promised not to, and what a good friend she was, the best friend, possibly, that she had ever had. She told her this, several times, and Licia agreed. Megan looked around at all the people she didn't want to see and found she couldn't focus on them anyway.

Some of Licia's friends were dancing. In their shimmery short dresses and bare legs they swayed dreamily, underwater flowers on long stalks. The rest of Licia's friends and Isaac were lined up on the couch watching in silence, as if it were a show they had sneaked into without paying.

Everyone's so dressed up, Megan said. She was wearing a skirt she'd bought from Oxfam her last year in school.

You look great, said Licia, not looking. Now you must mingle. And listen, if you speak to Benjamin, do tell him how pleased you are that he's here.

Megan watched the dancers, swaying a little herself. Mingle, she thought. After a while Benjamin came over looking for wine. He felt about for the corkscrew. Megan handed it to him, and he looked at her as if she had been deliberately concealing it.

I remember you, he said. Licia's friend.

I remember you too, she said. Licia's…Benjamin.

So, it's your birthday, he said. According to the invite.

It occurred to Megan that Xander had been wrong. Licia hadn't wanted to have this party so that she could ask Si, she had wanted to have it so that she could ask Benjamin.

He asked her what she was doing now, and she told him about the requisition forms.

You're still doing that? He stared at her. Really?

Just for now, she said. It's temporary.

Yesterday, Eunice had handed her an application form for a job on the next floor. You should apply for this, Eunice had said. It's more money.

It was a lot more money. It wouldn't hurt, Megan had thought, to be making more money while she was waiting for the very thing she wanted to come along.

How long has it been? Benjamin said.

It's not so different from Licia working in the gallery, she said.

Ah, but Licia, he said. It doesn't matter what Licia does. She's just going to get married to some rich guy and spend her days chatting up Tory wives while he screws the country.

Was he really an alcoholic, she tried to remember, or was that just one of those things Licia said?

You can't do things to order, she said. This had made perfect sense in her head. It's not like making cakes. That is, plastic buckets.

Don't get sucked in, he said.

I don't know what you mean.

When I get up in the morning, I have to work. Otherwise, I starve. It's a wonderful discipline.

I have to mingle, Megan said.

What did he know anyway. If his life was so great, how come he was an alcoholic.

She maneuvered around the dancers. The junkie gave her an evil look, so she steered around him too and found herself face to face with the Unwins.

Hi, Megan said.

They looked at her as if they expected her to add some witty repartee.

It's my birthday.

We knew it was somebody's birthday, said Mrs. Unwin.

Megan remembered the bins suddenly. She hoped they wouldn't start on that.

Are you the one who goes out early? Mrs. Unwin said.

I suppose I am. She had never been this close to the Unwins before. Mrs. Unwin was small and dark and pointy, Mr. Unwin was mousy and pale. Not much sibling resemblance.

And then there's the one who comes in late, Mrs. Unwin said. And the one who hardly goes out at all. The writer.

You do know a lot about us.

Oh yes. Mrs. Unwin seemed to think she'd said something funny. Out on that balcony. We hear everything.

They had been right underneath all along. How odd that she had never thought of that. In her imagination they took their refugee bodies into their flat and shut the door and ceased to exist.

It's been quite an education, said Mrs. Unwin.

Oh dear, said Megan.

Mrs. Unwin laughed again, touched her arm. Don't worry, we're only teasing.

At least you don't steal our mail, Mr. Unwin said.

They both laughed loudly at this. Not like refugees at all.

Of course, Neil works at home so much, Mrs. Unwin said.

He does? Neil must be Mr. Unwin. Who worked at the Inland Revenue.

Yes. His book. Virgil.

You're doing a book on Virgil? Megan stared at him. For the Inland Revenue?

They both looked at her, and laughed again.

Perhaps it was another branch of the civil service after all.

I have to mingle, she said.

Some time later, she found herself at the front door. She congratulated herself for having circumnavigated the room. The next thing must be to turn around and go back.

Xander was out on the balcony. His whole manner told Megan that he was sulking. He was holding a box of chocolates (her birthday chocolates!) and was engaged in taking a bite from each one, and throwing the discarded halves over the balcony. Nearby, Yvette was talking to the junkie. Megan wondered what he would think of *her* hands. Licia's friends were still dancing, arms drifting in the current. Licia was dancing now too, not with but in front of Benjamin. She swayed and sparkled and was in that light barely distinguishable from the other dancers. Benjamin watched her. Megan wondered if he knew about the house in Chelsea.

She found herself in the kitchen and saw her cake. From somewhere grand by the look of it, Harrods or Fortnum. Licia could have put it on The Parents' account. Megan had a vision of her mother's cake, with piped decorations, which she was good at, and candles. She shivered. Perhaps she had caught a chill from the open window. That's funny, she said aloud, and started eating cake.

When she came out, the music had slowed and the room was pitching and rolling in time with it. Air, Megan thought, and headed for the window. She started to hear raised voices.

Xander was still out on the balcony, and the voices were his and Mrs. Unwin's.

Extraordinarily inconsiderate, Mrs. Unwin was saying.

Xander was staring at her silently. He could get vicious when drunk. More than once Megan had seen Licia pull him out of a bar before someone hit him.

Unacceptable, said Mrs. Unwin.

People started to turn. Licia, seeing Xander in trouble, abandoned Benjamin and moved toward the balcony.

Throwing your rubbish into our garden, Mrs. Unwin went on. Wrappers. Apple cores. Bottles even.

Megan felt all of a sudden sober. She remembered tossing apple cores at the back fence. And an evening where they had sat spitting cherry stones over the balcony, competitively. They hadn't given the Unwins a thought. It was as if they had really believed that their physical elevation, arrived at by an accident of small ads and arrival dates, gave them the right to drop things on those who, by similar accident, lived on the ground.

At that moment someone stopped the music.

You are a peasant, said Xander in the sudden silence. You have a soul of mud. You should go back down the mine so we don't have to see your peasant face. .

Mrs. Unwin did not weep or swoon, Mr. Unwin did not shout or raise his fists. They both looked at Xander as if they were memorizing his features, and then Mrs. Unwin said, You are very drunk. We can discuss this tomorrow. And she turned round and so did Mr. Unwin and they headed toward the door.

I'll still be drunk tomorrow, Xander said to their backs. No, I mean, I'll be sober and you'll still be—

But they had gone.

The party broke up quickly after that. The music stayed off. People hugged Licia and thanked her, as if the party had been for her. Xander stayed leaning at the balcony, motionless except for his eyes, which kept sliding down and then twitching up, as if repeatedly surprised.

I feel so bad, said Megan, when Licia rejoined them.

What a calf, said Xander. Such a fuss.

But she's right, said Megan. I don't know what we've been thinking.

You would say that.

What do you mean?

He inclined his head slowly toward her. All peasants together.

Xander! Licia said. But she laughed.

Megan looked at her.

Licia shrugged. He took something earlier, she said. He's off his head.

My mind is perfectly clear, said Xander. Then he slid down the window frame and sat down hard and closed his eyes. Perfectly clear.

He may have stayed there all night. Licia turned her attention back to Benjamin and Megan took a bottle of wine to bed with her.

A week later it started raining. It soaked through the dust. It flooded along the gutters. It washed the withered leaves out of their corners, pushed them along the pavements, banked them up under walls and railings. All over the city, tidelines appeared, as if the sea had come through in the night.

Licia and Megan sat watching the rain pouring down the windows and collecting on the balcony. Megan told Licia how she used to imagine raindrops were conquering hordes, each new line of rain wiping out the line in front of it, and Licia told Megan she was moving into the house in Chelsea and Xander was going back to his parents.

What? Megan said.

His father's going to sponsor him. Let him finish his novel. So long as he lives at home.

Megan wondered how this could have happened when Xander hadn't talked to his father in years.

Si and I are going to choose the ring this week, Licia went on.

Megan thought of the money she'd borrowed from Licia and wondered how she would pay it back. Neither a borrower nor a lender be, her mother used to say. She wondered where she would live now. She thought of the hostel and how she used to put her purse under her pillow at night.

I'm sorry, Meggy Peg. You'll forgive us, won't you?

Is this what you and Xander have been arguing about?

You've got time to find somewhere else, Licia said. We've got this place until the end of the month.

You don't even fancy him. Megan had finally met Si a few days before, and it was noticeable that Licia kept twitching him off, absently, like a circling fly.

I can help you look if you like.

A stockbroker!

We'll still be best friends, Licia said. You and me. Kindred spirits. Nothing will ever change that.

These are the things Megan did that week. She took out the application form that had been folded in the bottom of her bag since Eunice gave it to her and threw it away. She bought an *Evening Standard* and circled some flatshares. She circled some job adverts too. Assistants to assistants to assistants. She took her jacket to the dry cleaners to have the gum removed. She spent the last of the money she didn't have on a pair of shoes that would stand the weather. She tied her hair back and studied her reflection and saw that she was the same as she had been. Then in her salvaged jacket and her waterproof shoes, she set out into the rain.

MEGAN ANDEREGG MALONE
Safekeeping

What they don't seem to understand is that I like things the way they are.

It's become very fashionable for people to appear on these television shows, these so-called reality programs about people BURIED ALIVE, people DROWNING IN THEIR OWN POSSESSIONS, obese old men surrounded by expired, unrefrigerated yogurt containers and wisp-haired, rail-thin ladies with dead cats rotting underneath piles upon piles of newspaper, everyone wringing their hands and psychoanalyzing and pitying, pitying.

I would never keep yogurt unrefrigerated, and all my cats are alive, thank you.

The thing I hate is when they come sniffing around in the guise of *helping, just stopping by, I was in the neighborhood.* Their neighborhoods are clear on the other side of Brown County, miles and miles away, only gangs and burned out factories in between. They aren't fooling anyone with their casseroles and their Learning Company books-on-tape.

I thought I was avoiding this whole problem by not having my own children.

There were certainly enough children to go around in my family, my brother and sister amassing seven each, boy-girl-boy-girl like clockwork every year and a half. They nearly bankrupted me, so much I spent on silver spoons for nearly two decades.

The oldest one, Roger, my sister's boy, comes nosing once a month, his big bristling mustache entering the room first. He doesn't knock, because he knows I won't answer. How he got a key, I don't even want to know.

"Gale," he says, using a nickname my sister, his mother, gave me as a child, in honor of my temper, "Gale, those boxes next to the doorway. You really should clear them out; if you had to get out in a hurry, you could trip and fall and burn to a crisp."

"Morbid," I say. I am supposed to offer him a drink, a cookie, some bridge mix, like a good little doddering maiden aunt. Instead, I gesture to the other chair at the table. He can sit if he wants.

The boxes are from my CSA delivery. Before the arthritis crabbed my hands so, I used to grow my own vegetables. My sunny backyard burst with crisp lettuces round and shiny as babies' heads, bosomy red tomatoes, impressively phallic zucchini and summer squash. I refuse to submit to the conspiracy of pesticides and engineered monstrosities inflicted on the ignorant public by big agriculture at the Piggly Wiggly.

My produce is delivered to me once a week by an earnest young couple named Aggie and Bo, poor things. They wear their hair in matted ropes like the ones that hang from the backside of my long-haired Maine Coon. They tell me they are "urban homesteaders." They give their chickens cute names, like Toby and Ralph. They offer me sour cheeses from the milk of the goats they keep in a vacant lot down the street from the old Lee Plaza hotel, honey from the bees they keep in improbable hives on the top of the vacant Kales building.

Someday, if I think of it, I will invite them in and tell them all about my own homestead, the outhouse with the Sears catalog for toilet paper, the lard sandwiches sprinkled with salt we ate to keep our stomachs from snarling too loud, the baby brother we lost to diphtheria in 1932.

We'll see how cute they think farming is then.

Roger opens the refrigerator to file away whatever he's got in his paper bags: cottage cheese, mandarin oranges in sugar syrup, sliced turkey wrapped in plastic, the bland and inoffensive things people feed to children and the elderly. He winces when he sees what's in there:

Opened cans of cat food, several jars of pickles, leftovers from the last few casseroles his wife sent over, jars of strawberry, blueberry, raspberry jam, bacon, sausages, pimento loaf, bologna, broccoli, cauliflower, rutabagas, kohlrabi, apricots, plums, pineapple, canned peas, creamed corn, milk, yogurt, cheese, sour cream, mustards, salad dressings, barbecue sauces, tuna salad, ham salad, chicken salad, egg salad, tofu, tempeh, seitan, olives, milk, buttermilk, prune juice, apple juice, cranberry juice, wine, vodka, gin, a very old can of Hamm's.

"Don't move anything around in there," I tell him. "Then I won't know where anything is."

He settles the bag gingerly on the counter, in a small open square of space in front of the microwave. I hope he doesn't open the microwave, as I have started storing extra pickles from Bo and Aggie's bumper crop of cucumbers inside. He won't understand.

"I want to take you up to the farm," he says, settling on top of a pile of magazines like an elephant in a circus sitting on a tiny stool. "Can we go today?"

Roger has driven his ridiculous gas-guzzling monster truck. I need him to lift me inside, clumsy and lumpy as a bag of flour. He refuses to drive my car, a hybrid, and I know why. He says it's because he has had trouble with trees downed in the farm road, that he needs his chainsaw and ax and four-wheel-drive and whatnot. I know it's really because he feels like it would insult his manhood or something to drive something so gentle, so quiet.

We take the shortest way, zipping up the thumb of Michigan like a stitch on a glove. There is almost no traffic. He doesn't speak and puts the radio on the classical station. I turn away from him so that he is just barely in my periphery, just the outline of a middle-aged man, belly protruding, hairline receding.

Looking out the window at the green and purple and yellow flashes of wildflower and weed, I can almost pretend that he is his father, Ed, my brother-in-law. They share the same bristling mustache, the same air of perpetual concern.

There were days we stole up together, usually driving the long way, over snow-scarred, bumpy roads, through the gleaming hard edges of Flint to the strip-malls of Bay City and along the silvery edge of Saginaw Bay. When we saw the sign for Bad Axe, we laughed, every time. Sinatra on the radio until we lost the Detroit stations and settled into static and comfortable silence.

Ed was a Pontiac man. Every two years on her birthday, my sister collected the keys to a new car, hand outstretched wearily, as if she were collecting Ed's unlaundered shirts. She had no appreciation for automobiles.

But I loved the leathery smell of a new car, the gentle bounce of a good suspension, the orderly rows of buttons and levers and dials that lit the dash like constellations. I'd ease my shoes off and tuck my naked feet up under my chassis, let the wind whip through the open window and pull my careful hairstyle apart. Ed would usually bring a thermos of Irish coffee and a tin of nightcrawlers for fishing. I would always rescue the tin, wash the soil and worm guts out of it, tuck it into my handbag to bring home and use again.

"Gale," he'd say. When he said it, it didn't sound like a blizzard or a squall. Maybe one of those afternoon rain showers they have on the Hawaiian islands, an inky blanket the clouds smooth down just for an hour or two, then roll away for storage.

"Gale, you're always finding a place for the things no one else wants." And Ed would smile at me, not condescending or patronizing, but rueful, as if he were one of those things and would like nothing better than to take his place among my towers of hat boxes, minarets of canned goods, stacks of sheet music and Sunday circulars. To be taken in for safekeeping.

"Why are we keeping the farm?" my sister would ask sometimes at holiday dinners, well into her third glass of wine. "An empty eyesore, an albatross. When's the last time anyone even went up there? We should sell it. Get a beach cabin. Better yet, a winter place in Florida."

I refused to discuss it. "Just because something isn't being used doesn't mean it's useless," I would say.

At the farm, Roger is mostly interested in checking window glass for cracks, blasting heat through the forced air system to make sure it is working, scooping up rag rugs and draperies for laundering. He seems to think of himself as the farm's caretaker, its curator, preserving its perfect shabby emptiness. I know that his wife endlessly bitches about how the place smells of mold and rat shit. To me, it simply smells like the Farm, only older: just like my nieces and nephews probably detect my own aroma altering over time, becoming thicker, drier, antique.

There is still a cast-iron woodstove in the kitchen, hulking beside the electric model we purchased in the seventies. My sister had lobbied to throw out the old stove at that time, saying it was a waste of space. My mother warmed her irons on that stove, heavy lumps of metal that mercilessly squashed the wrinkles out of our muslin school blouses, our Sunday gingham.

When Ed and I came up to the farm together, we burned our trash in it, secrets turned to smoke.

The stove stayed.

While Roger checks the roof for loose shingles, I open the door to the root cellar: a blast of musty, dampish, mushroomy air. Here is the farm smell. I close the door quickly, to keep it from escaping.

While we are gone, his sisters and wife creep into my house like cat burglars. They bring a Dumpster and park it around back, where I won't see it right away. They start with the plastic containers in the sink, not even bothering to sort through the various grades and make sure things were recycled properly. They move on to the dining table, blithely filing much of my opened mail and catalogs in the trash can. They purge the cupboards of perfectly satisfactory boxes of noodles, bags of rice, even paper napkins, which certainly have no expiration date. They scoop out the front hall closet, building a sand castle of mateless socks and mittens, sweeping them into boxes and toting them out to the hungry green monster lolling against the curb.

I know something has shifted as soon as we step in. The smell is off, an odor of disturbed dust motes, newly opened spaces. Two of the cats weave and writhe against my ankles, anxious and disoriented. I know that feeling, that muscle memory, the tingling in the fingers when one turns to reach for something that has always been there and is suddenly out of place.

The empty sink gleams and gapes at me. The dining table's surface is as barren and smooth as a frozen lake, a scratch in the finish glinting like a crack waiting for an ice fisherman to fall into.

I open the cupboards and wince at the Hitler-youth marching of spice jars and boxed meals, straight, orderly, dead-eyed. I fling the refrigerator door aside, see nothing but the cheerfully colorful labels of the food he brought earlier and white space, negative space, chilled nothingness.

I suppose Roger prepared himself for the expected comments: "How dare you," "Get out of here," etc., etc. So he is startled when I say, "Am I dead?"

"Gale?"

"Am I a goddamn dead woman already? This is what you do to the dead."

He says nothing, closing the fridge, taking a seat at the bald table. I can see his reflection in the finish, it's so clean, that damn mustache masking whatever his mouth is doing, just the way his father's did.

"We want to help you, Gale," he says.

I shake my head, hoping it keeps him from hearing the quiver in my voice. "You have no right," I say. "Not yet."

Shortly after Ed's death, my sister—never a great fan of clutter—began giving things away. First, she started with the clearly superfluous, things like deviled-egg platters, punch bowls, egg coddlers in her wedding china pattern, Hummels and Lladro and Precious Moments figurines of simpering children praying together. She'd sit in her chair in the kitchen, a juice glass half-full of wine next to her on the counter, waving her cigarette at her children, grandchildren, nieces, nephews. "You like it?" she'd say. "Take it." I'd watch the young people parading out of her house, their arms laden with Spode and silver, destined for the pawn shop, most likely. Her knick-knack shelves and china cabinets became echoey, spare, stark.

Then she moved on to the more necessary objects: pots and pans, bath towels, winter coats. She wore the same pantsuit day in and day out, the same open-toed sandals even in winter. The kids didn't want her old clothes, or Ed's—there was no kitsch value in the smoke-smelling polyester. So she toted baskets and boxes to the Goodwill, the Salvation Army, St. Vincent de Paul's, decades of memories to be sorted by retarded people and sold for two dollars apiece.

As her house hollowed, I haunted the thrift stores, searching out those things that might have belonged to him. I thought I had had his dimensions memorized, but none of the plaid shirts hanging limply on racks seemed to have arms long enough, or the buttons were wrong, or when I pinched the collar between two fingers the way I used to, the heft of the fabric was off. So instead, I would buy some mismatched dishes, a board game, a stack of old records by musicians I'd never heard of.

By the time the cancer had worked its way through all the twists and turns of her gut, my sister had almost nothing in her house. An ashtray. A bathrobe.

"I like it this way," she would say, jutting out her bony chin. "Gutted, like the factories downtown. Like me," she said, and she would laugh without showing her nicotine teeth.

And I amassed. I stockpiled. I sandbagged.

After Roger leaves, I stare into the white vacancy that is my refrigerator. The walls have been wiped down; there is a very faint smell of bleach. I can see the back of it, the mysterious electrical workings, the naked light bulb. The air on my cheeks is so cold and dry that it seems to have a sound, high and keening.

What I need is a beer.

And miraculously, it is there: nestled into the door along with a bottle of salad dressing and a glass Mammy full of syrup. Why they didn't throw it out, I'm not sure: perhaps its old-fashioned styling, nearly square instead of tapered at the top, the pull-tab triangular instead of round, had signaled itself as an antique. I take it out and set it on the desolate, shiny table.

The last time Ed came to visit me was the hottest day of the summer. My curtains were drawn against the sun, the house so humid that the air was drinkable. He brought a six pack of Hamm's from the grocery down the street, and the beer warmed so fast that we dropped ice into our glasses—clink, clink, the only sound.

We sat in armchairs in the living room—unpiled, then. We did not speak. I thought of the staring contests my sister and I used to have when we were children, eyes boring into one another, unflinching, unblinking, each waiting for the other to crack. We lasted through five beers—three for him, two for me—before he finally broke the taut line of silence:

"You know we can't."

I knew.

I took that last can from the six pack and placed it in the very back of the fridge, on the coldest shelf. It would be waiting there, icy and refreshing, when Ed decided to come back. It sat, waiting, hopeful, ready, for thirty-four years.

I wiggle the tab backwards, working slowly. It is flimsy, bendable, almost as if it is made of wet cardboard. Finally, it breaks loose with a faint crack, and I am a bit surprised at the fizzing sound that burbles forth.

At the sound, one of the cats—the calico—steps out from under the sideboard where she has been hiding. She leaps lithely up onto the table, gives the can a sniff, shies back, and hops down again when she realizes the snapping metal is not connected to a can of cat food.

I start to bring the beer toward my lips, my hand betraying the tremor that I now wear like my sister wore her wedding ring, thoughtlessly, shamelessly. But I think better of it; a beverage so aged deserves a glass.

I pour the beer sidelong into a reasonably clean old Mason jar, tilting it against the flow just as Ed taught me to so long ago. As I watch the amber slide from one vessel to another, I suddenly have a vision: my mother sitting on a stool behind the farmhouse, a newly killed Easter lamb in her hands, its throat slit, its blood draining into a galvanized pail.

I bring the beer, skunk-smelling and cloudy, up to my lips, and think: so much of it is this: the transfer of liquids, the movement of one state of matter into another, the rearrangement of molecules, the effervescence of things long stored. The emptying of a glass.

JERRY McGAHAN
Arlene in Five

1.

When the brindled cow was five, she got an infected eye. Arlene took her to the vet in Armstead to have the eye examined, perhaps removed. The brindled cow wasn't worth the vet bill, but she was a pet of sorts. Arlene loaded the cow into the horse trailer, delivered her to the vet's holding pen in back, gave her some hay and water, then unhooked the trailer and left to pick up supplies. When she returned several hours later, the vet had cut out some tissue surrounding the eye and shot her up with antibiotics, a wait-and-see measure. On the way out of town, Arlene remembered the wiring and receptacles Leonard wanted for a renovation project on part of the hay barn. She parked in the lot behind the hardware store and went in the back door. She returned to find the trailer door open and the brindled cow gone.

Haltingly, Arlene circled the truck; she found herself holding the bag of wire and receptacles out in front of her as if offering them to someone, a trade for her cow. She got in the truck, drove around the shopping center, then circled several of the adjoining blocks of the residences. She went back to the center and called the police. "Yes," the dispatcher said. "She's on her way down Holcomb right now, and she's got a crowd on her heels. You better get down there. Last I heard she was in the eight-hundred block."

"Tell them not to chase her."

"I can't get him on the radio. Go find them."

Arlene hung up and ran to the truck.

Arlene found scattered flops of manure in the seven-hundred block, but she saw nothing on ahead. She turned right. The trailer clattered behind. She slowed, found nothing east, crossed Holcomb heading west then and found them two streets across. The cow had collapsed on someone's lawn. Her tongue was out, her head sagging onto the ground. Several dozen children, some on bikes, clumped before her. Adults in twos and threes stood farther back out on the sidewalk and in the street where the police car, lights flashing, had lodged itself at an angle against the curb. It was like a parade, something festive. Arlene left her truck in the middle of the street and ran. "Leave her be," she yelled.

An elderly couple stood on their porch looking down at the stricken animal. The old man had a newspaper in his hand. She had on her apron. "What?" the policeman said. He was standing nearest the cow, his hands propped on his hips.

"Why did you chase her?" Arlene cried. "Look at her." She dropped to her knees alongside the stressed animal and caressed the big, sagging head. The cow's breathing was shallow and rapid.

"She was loose. How we supposed to catch her?"

"Not by chasing her," Arlene barked. She hears the hush, the change of mood like a cloud over the sun. "If you would've left her alone, she would've stopped. Look at her now."

"She was running. You don't make her stop by watching her run away. She could cause wrecks, damage people's yards. You're the one at fault here, letting her out."

"I didn't let her out. Who did this?" She glanced around. When several boys backed away a little, she glared at them.

"We didn't do anything," one said.

"I've got to get her back to the vet," she told the policeman. "Can you help me load her?"

"Of course. Look—"

But Arlene wasn't listening. She ran back to the truck. First, she angled the vehicle's nose across the street and into a driveway. Cranking first one way, then another, she backed the trailer up to the curb behind the police car, gunned the engine, and popped the trailer wheels up onto the boulevard. A few limbs cracked overhead when the top of the trailer pushed through the lower canopy of a tree. The policeman's arms flew out but she did not slow, backed the trailer directly to the cow. She got a rope from behind the seat. The policeman was saying something to the old couple on the porch. The brindled cow looked worse, all flopped out, her sides heaving. Arlene dragged out the little ramp from beneath the trailer, butted the back end under the cow's neck, then tied the rope around her neck. She gave the rope to the policeman, who was stooping over, watching. "You pull from inside the trailer. Let up when I tell you to let her breathe. Can I get help from anybody else to push her?" she called out. A small crowd, maybe eight or nine men and several women, drew forward. "Behind and alongside," Arlene directed, "just push her up this ramp." The cow could not stand. Grunting, most of them on their knees squeezed in alongside each other, their hands lined along the cow's backside, some hands atop others, pushed. The cow slid up the ramp and into the trailer. Arlene leaped out, waited for the policeman to exit, then slammed and latched the trailer door.

"Is she sick?" the policeman asked. "I mean, was she?"

"I got to get her back." She pointed off across the city, then hopped into the cab. She edged the trailer over the curb, and then accelerating evenly, sped away. But by the time she got to the veterinarian's, the brindled cow was dead, her tongue draped out, her legs kicked out straight.

"Why? Why would they do that?" she asked Leonard that night. They were sitting at the kitchen table. "Why would they chase her to death?"

"They didn't know, Arlene."

"I don't get it." Arlene couldn't stop shaking her head. "That poor old cow, that sweet, sweet animal. They just ran her to death. They didn't stop till she was done for."

"What do they know about cows? Just like kids from town when they come out here always wanting to chase the chickens."

"They had no sense. None of them. That policeman, he ought to know something about suffering animals. I don't know how you can defend any of them."

"Because I don't think they would've chased her if they knew it'd kill her."

"You can't say that, Leonard. You should of seen them lined up around her, watching her die. They weren't afraid for their lawns or gardens, or somebody crashing into her. They wanted some action. Like she was a sacrifice or something."

"Get a grip, Arlene. You got a right to be mad, but don't lose sight of yourself."

"I want to lose sight of myself. I lost the brindled cow today, and they all thought it was great fun."

"Well, you're going to have to get over it."

"I don't want to get over it."

"I know. Stew in your juices then. See where that gets you."

"Don't you do that smug thing to me."

"It wasn't me that killed your cow, Arlene. I'm going to shut my mouth now, till it's safe again."

"I hate that smug thing you do."

But Leonard wouldn't be badgered back into the ring. Arlene went out and stood on the back porch, let the cool night wind blow on her fire. The sky shimmered with bits of icy light. Take the arc to Arcturus, she said, drive the goddamn spike to Spica.

2.

"You going through something, Arlene?"

"Sit down. Get undressed."

He shook his head, watched her. "All the way naked?" His expression was something between astonished and apprehensive. "That couch isn't big enough for the both of us, Arlene. It's the middle of the goddamn day."

"It was big enough for us thirty years ago. So what if it is the middle of the day?"

"What is this? Something you been reading in those magazines?"

She stopped unzipping her pants. "What's the matter, Leonard? You're not interested anymore?"

His expression is quizzical.

"Don't you remember when it didn't matter? Remember in the hammock? The back of the pickup?"

"That's a long damn time ago, Arlene." But he was undoing his belt and watching her.

She slipped off her bra and then went back to her pants. So what if it was a long time ago? "Here, let me help you, Leonard."

"Get away. God, you're nuts." He turned, chortled.

"No."

"Goddamn it. Arlene, quit that. Arlene. Arlene…" he trailed off.

A few days later, he came in early for lunch. He sat on the couch, made half a wink, and wagged his head once, a "come on over here" wag. She told him the couch was too small, and it was the middle of the day. And then four months after that, there they were sitting in Doctor Snelling's new-carpet-smelling office getting told about Leonard's pancreas, and three months later Leonard Darr was gone. Just gone. He wasn't out in the barn. She could look out the window, and there was the truck, but he wasn't there, not out in the corrals, not in the house, not in the bathroom, not on the back porch looking for the mate to his glove, not in the refrigerator drinking from the orange juice pitcher. Nowhere.

3.

It was somewhere in between the knowing and the dying when her father-in-law came to see her. She heard his car approach and looked back over her shoulder to see him getting out, but she stayed on her hands and knees in the sweet William and dwarf delphiniums. Henry went up on the porch for the milk crate, brought it over, and sat on it behind where Arlene was weeding. "Looks like you're getting dirty," he said.

"Oh, yeah. I think your son is down in the machine barn."

"I'm here to talk to you."

"Oh." She lifted, sat back on her heels, pushed the hair out of her eyes with her wrist.

"Keep at what you're doing. I don't know what to say anyway."

"Having a tough day, old man?"

He swallowed, traced a long oval with his head, but wouldn't look at her. His eyes were red-rimmed and welling. "Keep at what you're doing," he demanded.

She obeyed, went back to the stringy-rooted plantain, taprooted dandelions and campion and cheeses, creeping Charley tacked down at every node—plickety-plick it said when she stripped it loose.

"How you bearing up?" he asked finally.

"I'm pretty numb, Henry."

"You ever break down?"

"Not if I can help it."

"No, neither does Lenora. What's your secret? Why couldn't it a been me, Arlene? I've had my run. He sold the cows, leased out all that work, and then this?"

She tried sitting back again. "I don't know, Henry."

"Don't look at me. I'm a mess. I can't sleep, can't eat, can't even goddamn drink."

"You should take something, Henry. Have Harold Snelling prescribe something."

"What's he doing with himself, Arlene?"

"I think he's just trying to live regular days, do regular stuff, with naps stuck in between." She stops weeding, stays on all fours, speaks to the ground. "I think he wishes he hadn't leased out the hayfields. Retiring wasn't something he was any good at anyway, and now he says it's just like waiting around for somebody to phone or something. Or come and get him. So he doesn't know whether or not to start anything that takes more than a day. You want a handkerchief?" she asked.

"No. Does he say anything about all the snits I had when he let the cows go?"

"No. He knows how hard this is on you."

"Goddamn it, Arlene, it's all I can do to see him. I want to hug him right through me, take his goddamn pancreas and jump in the river. Don't. Don't look at me."

She went back on her hands, plucking out tough little weeds. "You going down to the barn?" she asked finally.

"I can't." She heard him get up, his crying turning into little yelps. He put the crate back on the porch. He went back to his car, walking bent, a wire-figure that had been crumpled, mashed by some adolescent fit of temper.

4.

Nate and Jenny came in the back door. Jenny was whispering something. She would be six in a week. Arlene leaned back, peeked around the refrigerator. "What're you sneaking around about?"

"We brought you something, Grandma."

"What did you bring me?"

Jenny's face gathered around her mouth and nose, a belligerent smirk. She had something in her hands, hidden in the crouch of her body. Nate was checking the soles of his boots. "Don't worry about that," she told him. "I'm about to mop."

"Don't you want to know?" Jenny cried.

"Of course I do, but what's it going to take to get you to show me?"

With that, Jenny thrust out both hands, her face stretched vertically, as if waiting for a firecracker to go off. A toad squirmed, levered with little hands and arms at the sides of Jenny's fingers.

"Oh, my goodness." Arlene threw her hands up in mock terror. Jenny's laughter was a whinny.

"All right," Nate said. "Go put him back in the garden." He wouldn't look at Arlene.

"Let me keep him, Dad. I can keep him in my room. I want to take care of him."

"No. Put him back in the garden."

"Dad—"

"No."

Her lower lip thrust out fat and pendant, she sulked her way out the door. Nate's blunt gaze bounced off empty parts of the walls. "What's going on, Nate?"

He put his hands on his hips, stared at the floor.

"Shelby?" she said.

"Isn't back from Wind Flat. She was coming home last night."

"Sit down. Want some coffee?"

"No." He shuffled past, sat slumped at the table.

"She call you yesterday?"

"No."

"You don't know how she did?"

He shook his head.

Shelby rodeoed. She was a barrel racer and a pole bender. Nate was not a horseman. She rode, and he logged. He had his own logging truck, a cat, and a small portable mill.

Jenny came back in. "Whyn't you go back out?" Nate asked. "Out on the swings or something."

"I don't want to." She frowned at both of them. It was as if she'd been assigned to keep them from talking about bad things.

"Here," Arlene took a basket from atop the refrigerator and gave it to her. "Go fetch the eggs."

"I don't want to."

"Jenny," Nate said. He spoke softly, gravely.

"You and your dad can take a carton of eggs when you go," Arlene told her.

Still grimacing, Jenny took the basket and went out.

"What are you going to do, Nate?"

"I don't know." He still hadn't met her eyes.

"You don't think there's any way this is going to work, do you?

People never change that much, not in a hunk as big as she'd need to."

"You can say that?" He squinted at her then. "You can just say that about anybody?"

"Pretty much I can."

"Pretty much you can." He nods, keeps on nodding, a kind of reverberating.

"Would it work better if I tried to defend her?"

"Work better?" He spaced the words. Warned her.

"What do you need me to do, Nate?"

"I don't need you to do anything," he whispered.

"Yes, you do. You need me to tell you to let her go." She made a hiss, sucking in a breath, the noise of turmoil, of labor. "Or you think you need me to tell you to hang on. Which one, Nate?"

"Jesus Christ," he yelled, stood.

"Nate."

"Jesus Christ," he yelled again.

She hugged him then. But she was making a judgment. She wasn't ever going to tell him to hang on. She couldn't. Shelby, Shelby. They all said she treated her horses good, which would've been terrific if Nate and Jenny were barn animals.

When Jenny came back, she opened the door, then closed it again, waited outside with her basket of seven eggs.

5.

Having knocked at her door, he stood hang-dog at the top of the steps. His ill-fitting vest of faded hunter orange, not much more than a gaudy tie-on rag, made him look like a child playing dress-up. It was the season of orange, when men and boys stamped with the same bright color terrorized the countryside for five weeks. On rare occasions, a horse, mule, or cow fell to their prowess; llamas with their somewhat wild profile had to be painted orange or collared with a bell. In dry seasons, untended campfires at hunting camps burned acres of prairie and forest. Hunters left gates open or parked locked vehicles in front of them or blazed away at a herd of elk and sent the animals hurtling through successive sets of five-wire fencing, ripping out quarter-mile segments at every line. Boom boom boom, the guns sounded skyline to skyline from the weekend before Halloween to the Sunday after

Thanksgiving. On a dark Monday dawn it was over, and a profound stillness settled again like snow, invested this one small blessing upon the months of gloom ahead.

She opened the door. "Yes?" There were two certainties about this scenario of a hunter at her door: he was there to ask for something, and he wasn't going to get it.

"I shot an elk, a cow, on Clary Creek, but I only crippled her. She crossed your fence, and I followed her. I found her on a bed and shot her, but she's on your land."

"In the safety zone?"

"Yes, ma'am." He was in his forties, at least, a graying mustache, white sideburns, short hair, strong blue eyes that didn't edge away.

"You broke the law." She waited, but he didn't deny it. "You don't shoot in a safety zone. What good's a safety zone? How would you like to live with high-powered rifles blasting away in the neighborhood of your bedroom?"

"I couldn't leave her to die. I didn't want her to suffer. I didn't want the meat wasted."

"What the coyotes or bears get is a waste?"

"I couldn't do it. I couldn't just leave her to die."

"Then you gutted her?"

"I did."

"There's no blood on you." Most hunters looked like they'd bathed in blood, especially with an elk, plaques of red like baked mud on the hair of the arms running at times up to their shoulders, maroon patches on their knees and on the toes of their boots.

He looks at his hands and wrists. "I washed it off in the snow."

"Two guys I turned in last year told me they were following a cripple. I get that story all the time. What they had were fresh tracks, or they chased them over the fence, or saw them there, and snuck in. They got fined good, lost their licenses."

Elk were the worst; they drove these weekend mountain men off their rockers. Once on the highway, on the way to the Armstead, she was following a line of hunters' rigs—it was Sunday afternoon and everybody was on their way home—when all their brake lights went on. They pulled off, or halfway pulled off with their tailgate butts still out in the lane, several leaving their doors open. Out came the guns. Fumbling, running, they stopped at the fence and blazed away at a small herd of elk that had just crossed the highway. Arlene saw two cow-elk fall. She was out of her truck by then too, yelling. "You can't shoot from the highway. And that's posted land." The eight to ten firing away ignored her. She got out a pencil and a notepad, scribbled down five plate numbers, drove to the Eighty-Eight Bar and called Fish and Game. They sent several wardens, but by the time they got there, the hunters were gone. They found one dead elk, and the drag marks of two that were taken ungutted, and although all the vehicles had been identified, no one was ever arrested or ticketed. They all denied it. There was no proof. Arlene got into an argument with a warden, but had to be satisfied with the explanation that they didn't have the resources to pursue anything that wasn't red-handed or more than a one-time infraction. After that, she kept a disposable camera in the jockey box. What could be worse than letting slobs walk?

"I can show you the blood track," the hunter on her step offered.

She looked off over his shoulder. "Did you walk or drive here."

"Walked."

"Where's your gun?"

"With the elk."

"I'll take you to your truck. I want your plate numbers anyway."

"You can have them now. I just want you to know, no matter how this comes out, I would do it again. I won't leave a wounded animal."

"You can show me that blood track too, then." She watched for a reaction but got nothing telltale.

In her truck, she said, "Maybe we write on the safety-zone signs that if you want to hunt in this zone, all you have to do is send in a cripple."

"I understand your position. I wouldn't like it either. I suppose that this has happened to you more than once."

She gaped at him.

"Yeah," he said. "But I wasn't hunting along your fence line. Where I shot her was more than a mile from that boundary. She made a beeline for your place, where she knew it was safe. She was hit in the neck and went down, but she got back up and got into the timber. She lost a lot of blood, so I don't understand it."

Arlene kept glancing at him through half-lidded eyes. "Where is she?"

In the creek bottom, maybe two hundred yards from your last hayfield."

"By the old homestead?"

"Yeah, right, there's an apple tree there."

"How do I know you didn't backtrack, smear some blood?"

He frowned disbelief. She waited. He looked away from her, out his window at the plane of white. "Backtrack?" he said finally. She waited. "Look," he said, "there are places, clearings where I could see tracks quite a ways ahead, and I cut across, made shortcuts."

"Good."

He stared out the window, didn't say anything, his head and expression locked. They remained silent for a mile or two. "What are you going to do? If that makes a difference? I mean when you find out I'm telling the truth?" There was something testy, a little challenging in the tone.

She glared at him. "I was home minding my own business, all right? And now you're in my truck on your way to your illegal elk on my land. I have every right to my suspicion. And I have an obligation."

He got out, opened and closed the three wire gates for her, and at the last gate turned the hub on his side to get it in four-wheel. The snow was seven or eight inches deep with patches of ice in the low spots. When they crossed the hayfield, she still didn't know what she was going to do if there was a blood trail. No blood trail, and he was toast. Except she knew there was a blood trail. She'd been home watching a Broncos game. Now she was here, where there would be no good ending.

There was blood everywhere in the snow around the animal, pools with purple clots where he opened her, slashes of red where he laid out the liver and the heart, and then all the patches and blots where he must have washed up in the snow. He'd skinned around the neck and down the shoulders, pushed the hide out with sticks, and he had her propped open wide to cool. Arlene looked at the neck, the bloody hole, and then inside at the ribs, the killing shot there. The inside was clean of hair and blood, even the tenderloins. "How'd you get her so clean?"

"I carry a washrag. I washed her good with snow."

Arlene looked around again at the bloody snow everywhere. She could see where he'd wrung the rag. She considered the big animal again, her unmistakably feminine face, large eyes and ears, small well-shaped nose. He hadn't cut off the teats, a trickle of milk necklaced a bluish membrane. "The calf was with her?"

"There were three others. I assume one was her calf, but I didn't watch them. I was so focused on her, trying to make sure I didn't lose her."

She went back to the neck. The coarse, dark hair was tarred with blackened blood. "How do you shoot her in the neck without killing her?"

"God, I don't know." He pulled off his orange cap, brushed back his hair with the back of his wrist. "Missed every bone, missed the big arteries and veins. How do you do that?"

That was her question. "Let's load her. I don't want another truck in here."

He brightened. She glared back, but didn't say anything. I never asked for this power, she was thinking. I didn't want it. You did this.

At one point, when they were cradling the forequarters, the drooping neck and head, his eyes met hers, and there was something grateful showing, the way dogs look when they want affection. She moved her eyes down to his chin and attached there as they struggled trying to get the lower leg over the tailgate, then the head. They were both gasping when they got the carcass to a position where Arlene could wedge herself against it, manage alone for a moment, whereupon he vaulted into the truck, grasped the elk's ears, and in a series of lunges, edged the animal forward. Arlene pushed behind at the hindquarters, but she couldn't lift them. When they hit the stopping point of that maneuver, he leaped down and sidled up alongside her. In twin efforts, their bodies pressed side to side, they lifted, heaved, and slid the elk on into the bed.

"Wow," he said breathless. "Thank you."

No, she was thinking. She had her hands on her thighs, and she wouldn't look at him.

"Oh, you got blood on you," he cried, rushed her with a gob of snow, scraped at her shoulder and below, moving dangerously, mindlessly close to her breast. She didn't push him away. She watched his eyes until he glanced up at her.

When he got back into the truck at the last gate, she told him that she was going to report him, that they'd slide the elk into his truck from hers, but that he'd have to give the animal up at the checking station.

"That's the way it goes," he said, looking straight ahead, saying it like a recitation, what he'd memorized and couldn't go back on. He left it at that. They said nothing about the elk again. She didn't know what else they would take away from him, his gun, his license, his rights to hunt for so many years, maybe nothing but the elk. She didn't want to know. It wasn't her doing. She was the outside party. By the time she got home, the deal would be over.

It was, and it wasn't. She felt as if she had done something wrong, when she hadn't. She went by the rules. What was more useless than regret? Over the kitchen sink, she rinsed away the last trace of the elk blood from her coat, but she could still feel him, his hand scrubbing at her.

NANCY WELCH
Pretty

If Trudy had scooped the keys from Karl's hand, if she had trilled, "How about I drive this time," or if she had snapped, "You've got no business behind the wheel, you should know that by now," they would have been stopped at that light, Trudy fiddling with the vents as the mist crept up the windshield and Karl bleating at the morning news. They might not have even noticed the ancient station wagon emerge from the thick valley fog, its parking beams dim yellow, the scrape of dragging muffler smothered by thick air. Certainly they would not have sailed onto Route 7, Trudy crying, "Red! Red! Red means stop!" foot pumping madly at a brake that wasn't there.

But Trudy had been distracted, looking for the grade book she'd failed to return to her satchel when she finished with it the night before, vanished along with the thin pink sheet that would tell her which neurologist Karl was to see this morning and where. By the time she'd laid her hands on the latter, Karl was shuffling toward the garage. A thousand frustrations lay with the day before him: the too-hot sweater he can't wriggle out of, so it winds up bunched and binding his shoulders for the entire afternoon until Trudy gets home from school; the ringing phones whose callers hang up before he can find the word "Hello?" Even his feet are an upset, unresponsive as stones. Once he got himself moving so purposefully, Trudy didn't have the heart to stop him. In both hands he'd clutched the keys like a prize.

"I know!" Karl shouts. His foot comes down heavy on the brake, bringing their Toyota to a citizenly halt very nearly in the middle of Route 7. "You think I don't know what a red light means?" Trudy is reaching for the wheel, scrambling out of her seatbelt, no time to explain, with love and patience as the neurology nurses advise, that the light now lies behind them.

This is when the station wagon—rust-crusted white, a '76 Dodge, they will later learn—surfaces from the gloom. It skims past, not a breath beyond their bumper, so close Trudy feels vibrating up through her thighs the thumping bass of a tricked-out stereo. Staring at her, face pressed to a backseat window, is Pretty Lavallee from tenth-grade civics. For a moment Pretty's face, her eyes fishbowl-wide, looms before her. Then, with the ghostly car, she evaporates. Later, Trudy will not be sure how long it took, how many seconds slipped past, before she shook herself into responsiveness. Later, she will tell no one that, amid frantic instructions to Karl to pull over, they are switching drivers *now*, amid shaking relief that when they were first setting out, it had taken him some minutes to persuade his hand to insert the key into the ignition—because the absence of that small delay would have put their Toyota broadside in the station wagon's path—she noted with annoyance that Pretty Lavallee was heading away from, not toward, school.

"That was a car," says Karl, amazed, as Trudy drives them past car dealerships and strip-mall restaurants, a Hooters Karl some years ago tried to halt with a petition. "It nearly hit us," he says, his voice suddenly small.

He looks at her and smiles. It is a smile, tentative and sheepish and more than a little afraid, that always makes her melt. He gives this same smile to neurology nurses, PET scan techs, anyone charged with looking after him. It says: *You're not mad at me? You won't leave me?* Trudy hates that he can imagine such a thing, hates even more that she sometimes gives him reason. In hushed waiting rooms, she wants so much to be like the other spouses, tenderly solicitous, able to pass whole afternoons without a thought for anything except to hold her husband's hand, find him a fresh magazine. But her lunch break allows just forty minutes, scarcely time to collect Karl from whichever office she'd deposited him in before work that morning, return him home, get back in time to teach AP comparative politics. "Can you get the lead out," she once, to her horror, heard herself say. Everyone in the crowded waiting room startled and stared. Karl, who had been looking at his shoes and mumbling desperately, "Come on, come on," had looked up at her too. For a second it was as if she had slapped him. Then he gave her that heart-wrenching smile. Too late to keep the neurology nurse from making a note in Karl's chart—she would talk with Trudy next time about patience, understanding, and the benefits of counseling—she looped her arm through his and made herself take two steadying breaths before she said, "It's all right. Take your time. Shall we try again?"

"It's all right," she says now, reaching down to switch off the radio, the distracting morning news that will upset Karl more. There is the war he did not stop, the nuclear power plant he could not shut down. His appointment is at the hospital. It has a coffee shop where he can safely wait until her eleven o'clock break.

"But the light," Karl persists. "I went right through it."

A bank clock reassures her they've lost no more than a minute of time. "It's all right," she tells him. "Nothing bad has happened."

It isn't until her ten o'clock civics class that Trudy gives Pretty Lavallee another thought and then that thought is relief. This is the class Trudy teaches for students Graniton High terms *exceptional* and herds in courses in entrepreneurial enterprises and hospitality science. These are the students who, with or without diplomas, will either join the Vermont Guard and go to Afghanistan or else go to work in Route 7 strip-mall restaurants, the lucky ones landing jobs at one of the bigger car dealerships. A few, Trudy knew, would be plenty bright if their minds weren't hijacked by video games or snowboarding. Not Pretty. Every year there is at least one like her, girls who are forever tugging at too-short T-shirts whose inappropriate messages get them sent home. When they sit, their low-rise jeans display so much bare bottom that Trudy seats them in the back row. There they loll, their eyes, heavy with makeup, at half mast until they are awakened by the attention—any sort of attention will do—of a boy or until the wrong word from a teacher taps a vein of noisy indignation. Once when Trudy sent Pretty home to change out of a top no bigger than a postage stamp that declared *Objects Inside Are Larger than They Appear,* Pretty loudly proclaimed, all the way down the echoing hallway, that Mrs. Werbel had a dirty mind. Spotting the vacant back-row chair between Bernadette and Jasmyne, Trudy makes a mental note to mark Pretty's absence as soon as she finds her missing grade book. Then she gives the class a bright and hopeful smile, genuine and heartfelt, her day taking a turn for the better.

"It's because you're a good teacher." That's what Karl says when she groans while grading quizzes from her exceptionals. "You're patient with those kids. You make a difference."

Karl had been an environmental engineer. He measured wind, calculated its conversion to energy, then packed PowerPoints with indisputable evidence, including that of the apocalyptic consequences awaiting those who did not embrace ecological facts. Karl had always been animated by ideas so grand, hopes so rousing that for most of their thirty years together, Trudy imagined she looked up to him, even though in their socks they are exactly the same height. Still, he had failed, again and again, to persuade wary hill dwellers to accept turbines for their towns. What he did, he lamented, made no difference at all. It wasn't just cramped rural minds he'd been up against but King Coal, Big Oil, the corporate bullies of Hydro-Quebec. Trudy imagines them lined up as chess pieces, menacingly large, preparing to knock Karl's poor rook off the board. Meanwhile, his coworkers went for hamburgers at Hooters, and not even their own daughter—whom they'd spotted one night on the local news, among hundreds of protestors waving "Save Our Mountaintops!" placards—shares his values. Trudy doesn't tell Karl she wonders if maybe the protestors have a point.

But Trudy, Karl claims, can take a measure of her efforts with every exceptional who becomes an unforecasted success. When he was still able to work, he sat next to a student of hers on a flight from Chicago to Dallas/Fort Worth. She had been on the hospitality-science track at Graniton High, was now regional manager for a chain of East Texas Comfort Inns. The former students Trudy most often sees are those who push strollers along Route 7's bumpy shoulder or treat her and Karl to a complimentary Bloomin' Onion when they dine at Outback Steakhouse. The latest quiz she gave her exceptionals—*What is the purpose of the president's cabinet? What does the Constitution do?*—returned with answers like "To hold china" and "Sits in a museum." The video-gamers and snowboarders were just being wiseacres. That's what Karl would say. But when half the class wrote *the Bible* next to *What is the supreme law of the land?*, Trudy felt defeated by their sincerity.

Then she came to Pretty's quiz. At the top, the girl had scripted Pretty G. Lavallee in spiky letters, the *y* a triangle-ended devil's tail, the *t*s turned into ornate crucifixes as if hers were the name of a heavy-metal band. She had also written *bibel*, then, leaving the rest of the question unanswered, decorated her response with some of the book's more gruesome scenes. There was, predictably, the bloody head of John the Baptist plopped on a platter, needing only the addition of pineapple rings to be served up like a holiday ham. But also, unexpectedly arresting, was the image of a man whose arms lifted in fruitless effort against a shower of stones. Trudy had been impressed that, disturbing though the image was, the girl could draw.

Trudy hadn't marked the quiz with a grade. What was the point? But next to the Stoning of Stephen she scribbled, *I'd like to talk to you about this. See me after class.* She meant to ask Pretty if she'd considered signing up for art, looked into the technical center's program in graphic design. Trudy thought she might encourage her. Except then in the next class, she asked Pretty to name one of the three branches of government. She thought she had pitched Pretty a softball. The girl regarded her with an expression blank as a peach. "I dunno," she replied. "Maple?"

Karl chuckled when she told him. Or, more precisely, he chuckled two or three minutes later, after she left him in front of the television, bleating at CNN, while she washed the dinner dishes.

"Crooked," he quipped. "Now that would have been a smart reply. The three branches of government are crooked, crookeder, and crookedest."

His voice so startled her, the plate she was drying slipped from her hands. It bounced off the sink's edge, then smashed against the tile floor, breaking into neat triangles like pieces of pie. Conversations with Karl are like this now, an overseas phone call, his responses coming after a disconcerting delay. For a moment, he had sounded just like his old self, though the neurologists have explained that his old self is still in there, his mind perfectly intact. There is no point in shouting at him, "Red means stop!" because of course Karl knows that. She should save her breath rather than scold, "Hurry up, you're getting water all over the floor!" when he stands dripping on the bathmat, pondering the unfathomable distance to the towel inches away. One might as well stand scolding an outdated computer, its drives churning with the effort of retrieval. The TV news, which Karl spends too much time in front of now that he can no longer work, just makes it worse. It sends his brain into emotional gridlock. Instead of grumbling, "We're living in a goddamn plutocracy" or "When are people going to wake up and smell the emissions!," he can only bleat, "Bleh" or "Pooh." So when his voice came to her in the kitchen, sounding like a clear crystal bell and startling her into dropping that plate, her heart thrilled at the thought that by some miracle Karl had been restored. He would not get worse. He was getting better. Then she remembered that Pretty upset her, not him.

Trudy hadn't been convinced the girl had meant to make a joke, but that didn't stop Pretty, when the class burst out laughing at "Maple," from rising in her seat. Her theatrical bows pulled her perilously low-cut jeans lower still. From Bernadette, Jasmyne, and a few of the surrounding boys—the Thibault twins Trudy can never distinguish between—she accepted congratulatory palm slaps. As Trudy tried to soldier on, Pretty, emboldened, eager to entertain, waved her arm in the air, crying, "Oh, oh, I know that one! I know that one!" When Trudy ignored her, Pretty shouted out her answers. *What do we call the first ten amendments to the Constitution?* "Booo-rrring!" When Trudy reminded her to wait to be called on, Pretty protested, "You're violating my rights! I want a lawyer!" She made full and colorful use of her powers of speech as Trudy escorted her to the vice principal's office, but it is what Pretty turned and said to her just before she slouched through the door that Trudy will later recall.

"You'll be sorry," Pretty said.

"Believe me," Trudy replied, "I already am."

That first day Pretty doesn't show up for school, Trudy has the passing thought that she should stop by the office to say she has seen the girl and she isn't likely sick but truant. At odd moments through the day, the memory of that white station wagon emerging from the spectral fog comes upon her, making her shiver; she will need to be more vigilant about keeping the car keys out of Karl's hands. As for Pretty, Trudy decides she must have been suspended, even though her name isn't on the list. When Pretty fails to make an appearance the next two days running, Trudy enjoys the reprieve that comes when such a student—why fret over the reason?—isn't in school. No one strolls into her civics class eight minutes past the second bell. On Wednesday, the exceptionals even manage to have a reasonably good discussion about the struggle for voting rights. The "n" word is never uttered. When one of the Somalis—celebrated as *New Americans* in district news-letters, then slotted in with the exceptionals—registers his belief that everyone, even those not yet citizens, should be allowed to vote, his classmates listen respectfully and nod, not a one of them retorting, "Why don't you go back to where you came from if you don't like it here?" In her grade book—which she finally found, on top of the microwave; she'd forgotten she used it as a dustpan the night she dropped the plate—she notes Pretty's absences—they total eleven so far just for the latest nine-week period—and says nothing. She can't imagine Pretty will pass tenth grade, can't imagine facing her next year. Probably she will decide to drop out. It is no business of hers, of course, if Pretty Lavallee wants to get an early start on ruining her life. Although she always admired her husband for wanting to save the world, Trudy had let go years ago of the notion that it was her painstaking letters that got her *gifteds* into Princeton, that a robust appreciation for democracy opened up a future for her back-row students beyond Hooters, the army, or—whether as guard or prisoner—Marble Valley Correctional.

Then comes Thursday morning when Trudy ducks into the teachers' lounge before the first bell and someone says, "Did you hear about Pretty Lavallee?"

"I know I've had the pleasure of not seeing her in class," Trudy briskly replies, "and that's all I care about."

The instant the words leave her mouth, Trudy knows they are the very worst thing she could have said. Or the second worst, since easily she might also have answered, "As far as I'm concerned, she can disappear from the face of this earth," which is exactly what seems to have happened.

If it had been another girl—not a Pretty or a back-row Bernadette or Jasmyne—Amber Alerts would have gone out before the first-day tardy bell. If it had been one of the gifteds, her face would be stamped on milk cartons from Maine to Massachusetts. What an outrage, the teachers agree, that the police did little more than shrug when Monday at suppertime Mrs. Lavallee walked into the police station to report her car and her daughter missing, gone since early morning when Pretty drove to the Price Chopper for cereal and smokes. *She's probably with one of her boyfriends,* they'd said. But none of Pretty's friends have seen her, and she had still been in her pajamas—sweatpants and slippers— when she left the house. One by one Trudy's exceptionals are pulled from her ten o'clock civics class to talk with the two officers who show up Thursday morning.

None of the teachers, Trudy is relieved to observe, reproach themselves for not making more of what they'd all assumed was the girl's truancy. But when she says, "I think we saw her, the car, Karl and me, Monday morning," everyone turns. The vice principal gives her a narrow look.

"And you didn't say anything?" she asks.

The students make up for lost time. At lunch they transform into a shrine the corner of the Price Chopper parking lot. There, by the Dress Barn, a security tape has revealed the grainy figures of two men, pale as ghosts, one pressing Pretty into the station wagon's backseat while the other, a dark ball cap pulled low over his eyes, climbs in front, the Dodge rolling out of range. In a growing pile, Pretty's classmates drop Price Chopper carnations still in their stiff cellophane, plush bunnies and bears from a Big Lots baby bin, inspirational cards with their lonely candles and prayerful hands. A custodian climbs a ladder to change the school marquee to *Come home, Pretty.* Construction-paper signs taped to windows implore the same, Pretty suddenly as beloved as a Graniton High homecoming queen.

At these efforts, Trudy feels the prick of tears. True, many of these students have known and ignored Pretty since kindergarten. But at least they are trying to do something. In civics that morning someone among her exceptionals has placed on Pretty's desk a bag of Doritos and a bottle of Mountain Dew. Before class' end these items are joined by a half pack of cigarettes—not a discount brand but Camels, usually guarded like gold. Despite the school's new rules against junk food and long-standing ban, naturally, on all tobacco products, Trudy lets these offerings stay. If she could, she would bundle up her own new-born regrets and place them there with a note she does not have the words to write: *Thinking of you, I'm so sorry, Get well soon.*

"Is it true you saw her, Mrs. Werbel?" her students want to know. "What did she look like? Did she look scared?"

Through the school, rumors rip like remnant hurricane winds. Pretty has been snatched by New York City pimps or pornographers. She is drugged and locked in a trailer somewhere in Addison County. The FBI has been called, Border Patrol put on alert.

In the front row an ordinarily silent girl raises her hand. She is a girl Trudy suspects might one day shed her sullen Goth cocoon, go on to discover a cure for cancer.

"Why didn't you tell anyone?" she wants to know.

The police, tattled to by the vice principal, have already asked Trudy the same. Isn't she aware of mandatory-reporting rules? Didn't she realize something must be amiss when she saw Pretty being taken out of town? One of the officers—a woman, wearing a pantsuit instead of a uniform—tells her she'd had her for civics years ago. "Yes, of course," Trudy responds, as if she can place the woman among all those students over all those years whose names and faces recede behind her, grains of sand pulled out to sea. "Thank you," Trudy says, automatically, when the officer adds that she'd always thought of her as a dedicated teacher. Later she wonders if there was something else in the officer's tone, the implication that she'd been wrong about Trudy or that she had changed. By lunchtime her head throbs. What if she had marched into the office Monday morning? Would any of them have done more than roll their eyes at word of the latest absence of a girl who was never going to win an attendance award? Or what if their Toyota had been just a nose further into the intersection? Trudy pictures the white Dodge glancing off their bumper, spinning onto the soft shoulder and stalling, Pretty tumbling out into her astonished arms. Or could it be that somewhere beyond that intersection, Pretty had managed to pop the door, lies even now in a damp ditch of lupine, hurt, maybe unconscious, but unmolested?

Yet how swiftly any remaining doors of contingency are slamming shut. When her gifteds, fresh off a lesson about the power of citizen advocacy, lobby for class time to make *Missing!* posters to tape to lamp-posts, Trudy relents, although it now appears unlikely that Pretty is still in the state. In Massachusetts, troopers report, a rusted-out Dodge station wagon was caught on tape late Monday morning at a Berkshires Sunoco. Into the camera, which he must not have known was there, peered a man, his eyes so close they seem to swim. The image airs with the noontime news. Someone puts it on YouTube, and in classrooms, students huddle over smartphones and iPads. For once, Trudy and the other teachers let them, joining in to watch quietly, then turn away, Trudy fishing her own phone from her purse to call Karl. He, too, is watching the news. The local stations alternate between a class picture Pretty's mother must have provided—a younger edition of the girl Trudy has taught, wearing just the first hints of eyeliner and a Graniton Growlers baseball shirt—and the Sunoco station man—hardly more than a boy really, with a spray of pimples across his chin, one cheek puffed with chew or perhaps a badly abscessed tooth. When Trudy explains to Karl why she's taking him to the police station after school, that they are witnesses who saw the car leaving Graniton, he doesn't reply. Then just as she's about to hang up, he says, "Terrible. Imagine. If we'd only known."

By midafternoon the boy has a name and a last known address, a stepfather's apartment in St. Albans where police found a scrawled *Gone hunting* note taped to the door and inside, a man one might take to have been asleep at the kitchen table, head resting on scattered playing cards and wads of burnt foil, except that he had a knife in his gut. Now the news airs interviews with St. Albans neighbors speaking of a Sunday night stereo, fighting, a party gone south. Graniton girls who've never given Pretty a glance ("What the fuck are you looking at?" she would have said) now quietly sob. The gifteds search for Pretty on Facebook and, not finding her, create a page for everyone to "like." Bernadette, Jasmyne, and the Thibault twins have fled, the Thibaults to stand vigil at the Price Chopper memorial, Bernadette and Jasmyne to sit with Pretty's mom and aunt in their duplex on River Road. Over the intercom the vice principal calls everyone else to the auditorium—there is no point in trying to teach—where, when the senior class president takes advantage of the evident relaxation of rules and asks everyone to pray in Jesus' name, even the New Americans, mostly Muslim and Buddhist, bow their heads. The auditorium is dim except for the lighted stage, but up and down the rows tiny screens glow. Phones buzz with the latest: a trucker who's turned up to say he gave two young men a lift down I-89, dropping them at the exit near the Price Chopper because it was past six in the morning and one of them wanted to buy beer.

Trudy tries to imagine Pretty using her words. That's what she sometimes says, exasperated, to Karl—*Come on! Use your words!*—as if he is a toddler. Maybe Pretty has coaxed the boy, the other man, into smoking a joint, drinking a few beers, and then, once they passed out, car parked on the side of some dirt road, she slipped away. Maybe she is trying to make her way home, disoriented, fighting the effects of concussion or shock. Maybe she is hiding, too frightened to come out.

But when Trudy brings Karl to the station after school, the woman she'd spoken with earlier greets them at the busy front counter with the news that she's just gotten off the phone with western Massachusetts. Troopers have found the men in North Adams, in a closed-for-the-season tourist cabin they'd broken into. They hadn't been armed. The younger of the pair, western Massachusetts reports, seems ready to talk.

"Pretty?" Trudy asks. She almost doesn't. The officer's face looks gray, her cheeks sagging. If she had been a years-ago student of Trudy's, it must have been when Trudy herself was fresh out of college. On the counter she lays a yellow legal pad. Above scribbled notes is written and underlined *Pretty Girl Lavallee.*

"He says he can show us where they left her," the officer replies, voice flat, then fixes her attention on Karl. Somehow, in the time since Trudy called him from school, he managed his own way out of the jeans and flannel shirt she'd helped him into that morning. He is dressed in his engineer's best, pressed khakis, a V-neck sweater over a neatly knotted tie. But as the officer starts with her questions, he grows agitated. He begins to bleat. Again, as she had that morning in the vice principal's office, Trudy tries to explain to the woman that there is no point. Given the fog-shrouded highway, the slowed circuits of his brain, only she saw the car, Karl its echo. She grips his arm protectively. "There's really nothing he can—" she starts to say when out of the blue Karl finds his words.

"Mets cap," he says.

Trudy drops his arm. If she'd held a plate, she would have dropped that too.

"Mets cap?" The officer gives him an encouraging nod.

"The driver," Karl says. "Not the younger one at the gas pump, but the other one. He wore a blue Mets cap. He had dark hair, long. It hung straight, not quite to his shoulders. And he had a tattoo. It ran down his left forearm. His window was down, and his arm rested on the door. Something skinny, maybe a snake, but they went by too fast for me to make out what it was or what he was wearing, except I could tell it was a T-shirt. It seemed like he had torn the sleeves off."

Trudy is struck with amazement: how much he takes in! She gazes at him with the sensation she had when they were first married of looking up. She is struck, too, with sadness: how little—less and less—he says these days, so rare moments like this take her by complete surprise. But perhaps, she considers, this is because it is less and less often she tries to talk with him, has ceased to think of him as someone with anything to say. Last night, for instance. She fixed supper, brought him to the table, took away the empty plates, returned him to the couch, all without saying more than, "Come on now, let's get you some meatloaf and salad" and "You watch your TV now. I have papers to grade." Or this morning when she said, "Into the tub you go" and "OK, let's pull up those pants," in just the voice she had once used with their daughter, long grown and gone, before she had learned to talk. "Oh, we're fine, your father's fine," Trudy says when their daughter calls. She lives in the far reaches of the Northeast Kingdom, in a town straddling the border with Quebec. Although that is one reason she rarely visits, Trudy had noticed that on the phone she, too, had asked less and less if she could speak to her father, then not at all.

Trudy tries to take his arm again, squeeze it with appreciation, apology, but Karl pulls away. He looks at her and the look is defiant, accusing too, as if he knows not only that she has sometimes given him reason to believe she could leave him but that she has imagined it too, pictured her own life at the end of this terrible tunnel they are in.

"Anything else?" the woman asks. "Any*one* else?" When Karl shakes his head—no hesitating, no delay at all—she adds, "Do you think you could pick him out if we got together a lineup tomorrow?"

In the pause before Karl replies, "If I can take my time," Bernadette and Jasmyne crowd through the station door with two women who look like older versions of Pretty, one heavier and one much thinner, both with hair Trudy learned from her mother to call dirty or dishwater. The heavy woman—Trudy has never seen her before, only the parents of gifteds show for conferences—has a tear-swollen face. She leans on Bernadette who appears to be helping her walk. The other strides ahead of the rest, her jaw set, fists balled. "Where's my niece?" she calls out to the room, approaching the desk before another officer intercepts and shepherds them to a bench. They have been called in, Trudy gathers, to be told the latest, about the boy willing to show them where they've left Pretty. *Where they left her.* That's what the officer said, leaving open one last window of chance. Trudy's mind leaps toward it. She conjures up Pretty sitting in pajamas in a cheap motel, eating a bowl of improbable ice cream. Her heart reaches across the room to the woman Bernadette is helping to ease down on the bench, a mother who once upon a time had regarded her newborn daughter and decided, of all the world's lovely names for girls likely to live hard lives and meet harder ends—the Fleurs and Gabriellas, Auroras and Destinees—her name should be Pretty. Pretty Girl. How her heart must be shredding itself with her own *what if*s and *if only*s: if only they had not run out of cereal, if she had forbidden Pretty to smoke, if the police had only listened. Trudy is seized by the impulse to cross the room, embrace her.

Then, just at that moment, the station turns quiet, not a single phone ringing or drawer slamming shut, and when all sound has ceased, the whole room tense for news, the officer says, "Let me make sure, Mrs. Werbel, I've understood. Monday morning, two hours before Pretty reached..."—here she pauses—"her destination, you and your husband saw her being driven away in that station wagon, and you decided not to tell anyone?"

It is not likely to have made any difference. This is what they learn, soon enough. By the time Trudy walked into her Monday-morning civics class, Pretty was already dead, her body abandoned in a Berkshires quarry, just over the Massachusetts line. The boy, as he promised, as if being helpful matters now, leads troopers there before Thursday's sun goes down. He explains that, weaponless, they'd had to resort to boots and stones. It had not taken long. At least that's what he says. For a few days the shrine in the Price Chopper parking lot continues to grow, then becomes rain-sodden and tattered until someone orders it cleared away. For a few days at school, students whisper, in awed voices, the gruesome details. From these Trudy shuts herself away as much as she's able. She is haunted enough by Pretty's face, pressed to the window, catching the last glimpses of her life. There is the memory, too, of Karl, beside her in the police station, flinching, taking a full step away from her but not managing to say, not until they were halfway home, "You saw her? You saw her in that car, and you didn't say a word?" In that moment, it came to her that if one of them were ever to leave the other, it could be Karl leaving her.

But soon enough, within a few weeks or months, Pretty becomes another girl who died. There was one last year, a ninth-grader who'd been neither *gifted* nor *exceptional,* pulled from a pond where her uncle had sunk her after a rape gone wrong. There will be more— casualties, says Karl, of a sinking economy, a culture that worships Hooters and war. He says this as they sit at the kitchen table after supper and talk. They do that now, sit and talk, Trudy making the effort, taking the time that conversation with Karl requires. She is considering retirement. She now believes she has been teaching at least one year too long.

"If you get bored hanging around the house," Karl tells her, "you can join us."

He means outside the courthouse where now, instead of sitting home, bleating at the noontime news, he stands with Sisters of Mercy and leftovers from Vermonters for Peace. Because they carried Pretty over a state line, making it a federal case, the boy and his companion face execution. The coming trial has lifted Karl's sense of social justice like a helium balloon. On hearing days he stands with a sign: *An eye for an eye makes the whole world blind.* Their daughter calls to say he's famous, she saw him on the evening news. But when Pretty's family passes by, he tells Trudy, her mother spits on his shoes.

"What if they call on me to testify?" he asks. "What if they use my words to put two men to death? Do you think I could live with that?"

As he talks, Trudy listens. These conversations can take hours. They can take all night. She is practicing at being in no hurry. She is remembering a time when Karl, full of youth and purpose, used to tell her she shouldn't teach civics, how government is supposed to work, but instead American history—McCarthyism, COINTELPRO—what their government actually did. Recently he and their daughter have reconciled over the issue of wind, which has turned out to be every bit as corporate as coal, dirty as tar-sands oil. Some nights now Karl goes out after supper, Trudy driving him to meetings to plan a "Save Our Mountaintops" rally to be held at the same time as one in West Virginia. When Trudy asks the neurology nurse if he should still be doing things like this, picketing the courthouse and planning rallies, the nurse replies that it probably helps, mental stimulation against the coming lockdown. As for herself, she tries not to look ahead into the future's fog. The trial could be two years or three away. Karl may no longer be able to walk or talk, focused on the effort of every breath.

"Do you think I'll be able to live with myself?" Karl asks again, then pauses, not searching for words but awaiting her response.

ABOUT PETER HO DAVIES
A Profile by Douglas Trevor

The novelist and short-story writer Peter Ho Davies was born in 1966 in Coventry, England. Peter's father had grown up in North Wales and Peter spent most of his boyhood vacations there with family, amid countryside he has described as beautiful but also—from a boy's perspective—"slightly dull." His mother was of Chinese descent and met Peter's father in Malaysia. After marrying, the two of them settled in England. As a young boy, Peter wrote science fiction stories in his spare time, and excelled at mathematics and science. He did a joint honors degree in physics and the analysis of science and technology at the University of Manchester, before going on to Cambridge University, where he earned a BA in English.

In the early 1990s, after having worked in Malaysia and Singapore, and having served as the managing editor for the university newspaper in Cambridge for a couple of years, Peter moved to the United States to pursue an MA in creative writing at Boston University. This was his first trip to the States, and with the exception of returning to England and Wales to visit family and friends, Peter has never really left. Shortly after he completed his studies at BU, Peter's first collection of stories, *The Ugliest House in the World,* was published by Houghton Mifflin. The book won the John Llewellyn Rhys and PEN/Macmillan Prizes in the U.K., as well as the 1998 H. L. Davis Oregon Book Award. Peter's second book, another collection of stories entitled *Equal Love* (Houghton Mifflin, 2000), was a *New York Times* Notable Book of the Year and a finalist for the *Los Angeles Times* Book Prize. His third book, a novel entitled *The Welsh Girl* (2007), received a litany of praise from reviewers and was long-listed for the Man Booker Prize.

Peter's short fiction has garnered multiple Best American Short Story awards (1995, 1996, 2001) and an O. Henry Prize in 1998. In 2003, *Granta* magazine named him one of twenty "Best of Young British Novelists," and in 2008 he was awarded the PEN/Malamud Award for achievement in short fiction. Since 2000, he has taught in the Creative Writing Program and the Department of English at the University of Michigan. In April of this year, Peter came by my house in Ann Arbor for dinner, after which we had a wide-ranging conversation about his life and career as a writer. What follows are some of the topics we covered.

DT: So, Peter, having lived in the States now for more than twenty years, how do you see yourself? Are you a British writer? A British expat? An English writer with a Welsh background?

PHD: I certainly don't identify as English, per se. I'm more comfortable with the designation of *British* as a person. *English* seems a little too narrow for me, with my Welsh father. And *British* both embraces the Welshness and, as a term, has evolved to embrace something more multicultural than when I was a boy. But the British *writer* thing is trickier because while some of what I have written meditates on Britishness, I feel as if I had to come to America to become a writer, I had to get away from Britain, away from a nonwriter version of myself. It was necessary to get away from people who knew me as a physicist, or a friend, or son, and to reimagine myself. The exposure to American writers and writing also made a big difference when I first came to the U.S. The exposure to the short story form, which I associate with America in part because there are so many fewer venues for publishing short fiction in Britain, was particularly important. Because I identified as a short-story writer, and still do to a degree, American short-story writers really resonated with me. The models careerwise for me were more rooted here than in Britain.

DT: The novella in your first collection, "A Union," seems to some degree a companion to, or preparatory for, *The Welsh Girl*. It's about the effects of a slate quarry strike in turn-of-the-century Wales. We see the aftereffects of a similar strike looming over the town in *The Welsh Girl*. Esther's father, Arthur, lost his job at the mine as a result of the strike (although he ends up returning to work at the mine late in the novel). Were these motifs that you thought you might return to?

PHD: "A Union" certainly felt like something of a prequel to *The Welsh Girl*. While it wasn't planned that way, it was a touchstone for me during the writing of the novel. The villages, for example, in both, are more or less the same, just separated by forty-five years.

DT: Were you thinking consciously about writing a historical novel when you were working on your first collection?

PHD: No, I wasn't thinking even about writing a novel. I had no idea whether that collection could be sold. I remember I put it together a year, maybe eighteen months, after I had finished at Boston University. I think I had sent a few query letters to a couple of editors in Britain. And then, "The Ugliest House in the World" appeared in *Best American Short Stories* (1995) and Janet Silver at Houghton asked if I had a book and I sent her some of the stories. *OK, she said, those are interesting, but do you have a novel...*

DT: That is the curse of the short-story writer. You produce a story and they ask for a novel.

PHD: Right. But Janet, thankfully, said to come by and have a chat. I remember distinctly telling her that I knew she wouldn't be able to publish the collection in the States because it was too British, and when I went up to have lunch, my intention was to ask her for recommendations of people in England to whom I could send the book. Instead she offered me a contract.

DT: How did the idea for this novel—set in Wales during the end of World War II—emerge, then? Had you started *The Welsh Girl* while you were still working on *Equal Love?*

PHD: No. I'm not great at starting a book when I'm working on another. When I had finished *Equal Love,* I did feel from a career perspective that I had run out my string with collections. I had already published two in a row, and I had ducked the writing of a novel as long as I could. And I felt as if I was more or less ready to do it—or at least was ready to welcome the challenge of it. But the first novel I tried to write after *Equal Love* is actually close to the material I'm working on now: a historical novel about the Chinese in nineteenth-century America. But then I decided that the twin challenges of researching the historical space and still finding my feet in the U.S. were perhaps too great a leap to take at that time.

DT: I've heard you talk about this project as focusing on the Chinese who worked on the transcontinental railroad. Was the project initially imagined in broader terms than that?

PHD: Well, even when Janet and I were talking about *Ugliest House,* we worried—or at least I worried—that there needed to be a "hinge" story. There are these stories in Britain, and these stories about Chinese people in Malaysia, but nothing really tying them together. I had a story in mind for a while that would try to bridge these two spheres but it never quite worked. Still, even afterward, I was looking for something that would encompass those two distinct heritages represented in my first book. The story of the construction of the transcontinental railroad appealed to me for obvious reasons. There were the Chinese building the line from the West, and then there were the Irish (I would have smuggled a Welshman or two in there) building from the East. For a time, this novel was called *The Great Race.* But what I learned as I did more research was that the two railroad lines were in fact very different beasts. And the research required began to present itself as a major undertaking that I wasn't really ready for. The thing about *The Welsh Girl* that is slightly embarrassing to remember now is that it was supposed to be a more *manageable* first novel. It was a small stage, in an area I knew well, connected to things I had done before. It was supposed to be my quick, small novel. Eight years later—longer than World War II itself lasted!—it came out.

DT: So Rudolf Hess plays a significant role in the book. Was it planned at the very outset that he would figure prominently? I ask because that's such an audacious move to make as a writer, to inhabit the mind of a Nazi henchman, and of course a lot of the reviews lingered on the deftness of your portrayal of him.

PHD: No, it was an ongoing question up until almost the eleventh hour as to whether he would be in it. It wasn't in my mind at the outset. I had worked on the book sporadically for maybe a year or two. I found it hard to keep the momentum going, particularly when I was teaching. Usually in those stuck moments you feel like you need to be reinspired in some way. For me, that's a good time to do more research. And the research was really varied: about what it was like to be Welsh in that time, to be a prisoner of war, and so on. I read some narratives about POW camps, during which Karsten, the German prisoner in the book, began to assert himself narratively. I hadn't planned on telling any of the story from more than one point of view, not to mention his, but then I changed my mind—

DT: Initially, Esther's point of view was going to govern the whole book?

PHD: Yes, that's who I could really see at the beginning. But I didn't plan the novel out very much. "A Union" had been my only previous experience in writing anything long and that had just flowed. *The Welsh Girl* came together with much more difficulty. Hess made his entrance in a later stage of research. What I was struck by was, here was Rudolph Hess—the most famous German prisoner held by the British—and he was imprisoned in Wales. So I read some stuff about him, and I think I was probably drawn to it for a few reasons. The broader scope of the war wasn't fully represented by these guys in the POW camp. I wanted to remind us of where they had come from, what they had fought for. And I didn't just want to look at ordinary soldiers. I wanted to look at someone who gave the orders. It almost felt like an ethical imperative to do so. I wanted to allow for sympathy toward some of my German characters but not to what they were fighting for.

DT: Was Karsten's escape from the camp in the original plan? I ask because I recall wondering, the first time through the novel, how Karsten and Esther were going to build any kind of relationship, set apart from one another to the degree that they were. The possibility of escape didn't occur to me. The prisoners in the book dismiss it. And, ingeniously, Karsten doesn't talk about wanting to escape. The novel certainly doesn't feel like it's about to turn into *The Great Escape*. But when Karsten hops the fence, basically to spend some time by himself, it made perfect sense to me that he would do that.

PHD: Well, it wasn't in the plan originally. Initially the idea was for Esther and Karsten to spend a lot of time together working on the farm, which German POWs did in Wales toward the end of the war. I thought their relationship would spring up from that. The first draft of the book was about 550 pages long, of which pages 300–450 were about them working on the farm. There was a lot of sheep farming stuff! And in that version the temporal scope of the book would have gone from 1944 to the 1980s. I thought of ending with the jeopardizing of the sheep-farming business by Chernobyl fallout on the Welsh hills.

DT: So why did you scale back the novel in the manner you did?

PHD: Well, actually, when I took out those scenes, I rewrote them into the story that became "The Bad Shepherd" and actually appeared in *Ploughshares*. That was the title of the novel for a while—though it began to fit less when the center of gravity shifted away from Karsten's time working on the farm. What probably derailed the book for me was what happened to Esther at the beginning. I always had this scene, in which Esther was raped by an English soldier, in mind. In fact, I wrote that scene as a separate story that also ended up appearing in *Ploughshares* as "Think of England." One of the reasons I sold the piece as a story was that I wanted to get out from under it. Rape is so consequential that I felt it was shaping the opening of the story too much, when all I really wanted to do in the early pages was introduce the characters to the reader. But after the story appeared, and got picked up for *Best American* in 2001, I felt that I had to keep it. And then I kept struggling to know what the consequences of that act would be. It took me two or three years to accept that Esther would become pregnant from that encounter. And once I realized she was pregnant, the temporal scope of the narrative changed. The idea that the book was going to be decades long no longer worked for me. *No,* I thought, *it's going to be these nine months that the book will focus on.* The 550-page version of the book was huge and unwieldy—a kind of "kitchen-sink" draft—and no one liked it, myself included. So I radically cut that back to a draft that was only 150 pages long. Just Esther. No Karsten, no Hess. That allowed me to focus on her narrative from the rape on.

DT: In a different vein, the idea of nationalism, which you are really working through and thinking about throughout the novel, emerges in relation to shame. I'm thinking about when the constable of the town needles Arthur—Esther's father—by saying, in relation to Karsten, "Your enemy's enemy, is that it?" That kind of *is* it, isn't it?

PHD: I knew that before the war, Welsh nationalists had some ties to Italian fascists. There was a sense, in my own family, that Welsh nationalism was a kind of benign nationalism: arguing for road signs in Welsh, defending the culture, those kinds of things. I still think in many ways it's an honorable cause to argue for, and defend, such things. But I was interested in bracketing that kind of benign nationalism with the most evil form of nationalism: National Socialism. And I was interested in how these different kinds of nationalism might encounter one another.

DT: In a sense, the English represent as significant an enemy in the book as the Germans. The English "invade" Wales during the war, not the Germans, and so on.

PHD: Well, I'd like to think of the book as to some degree an equal opportunity offender. Welsh people can be offended, and German people, and English. Oddly, while I am neither Jewish nor German, Rotheram, the German Jew who works for British Intelligence as an interrogator, is the character I most identify with. His divided loyalties, his split inheritances. One of the reasons I struggled so much to finish the book, and why it was so long for a while, was because I wanted there to be a somewhat hopeful ending, for the sake of these characters I loved. And yet I didn't feel that Esther and Karsten could end up together; it wasn't quite in their stars. He would go back to Germany, to his mother. She would feel, after having claimed Rhys as the father of her child, that she couldn't ask for anything more. But it was agonizing to write this from either of their points of view. But once I approached through Rotheram's more distant point of view, I felt that I could finish the novel, because through Rotheram we can see these lives in the broader context of the war's losses. Everyone has lost loved ones. So the fact that Esther and Karsten don't end up together, while certainly sad, has to be considered against the scope of all that has been lost, and Rotheram could do that for me.

DT: Say more about what you are working on now.

PHD: I'm under contract for the historical novel on the Chinese in the U.S. that I mentioned earlier, and a collection of stories. The novel is going to come first, although I'm still a little ways off. Half of the collection is done. Some of the stories feel as though they are composed in the wake of *Equal Love*—they orbit around parental/child questions—but they're all stories that bump up in some way against contemporary evils, or at least what we label as evil.

DT: One last question. I haven't asked you anything about your teaching. Is there anything you find yourself saying to your students on a regular basis?

PHD: I hope I'm not that given to general advice, because when I teach, I like to keep the specifics of whatever text we are studying or workshopping in front of us, but something I do find myself repeating to students now more than ever is Flaubert's idea that talent is long patience, which I never understood when I was younger. The talented young writers we work with, however individual they may be, tend to have at least one thing in common. Precisely by virtue of being young and talented, they do not have very much patience. We are used to thinking of youth as the enemy of patience, but talent is probably the real enemy of patience. We think of talent as an accelerant, after all. So one of the things I try to emphasize is patience, including patience in the revision process. Waiting it out. Trying to hang around with the story or novel long enough to find the layers of complexity and depth that were not first apparent to us. That's something I find myself returning to a lot, for myself—*The Welsh Girl*, of course, was a hard lesson in patience, if a worthwhile one—as well as for them.

Douglas Trevor is the author of the novel Girls I Know *(SixOneSeven Books, 2013), and the short-story collection* The Thin Tear in the Fabric of Space *(University of Iowa Press, 2005).* Thin Tear *won the 2005 Iowa Short Fiction Award and was a finalist for the 2006 Hemingway Foundation/PEN Award for First Fiction. He lives in Ann Arbor, where he is an associate professor of Renaissance literature and creative writing in the English Department at the University of Michigan.*

LOST ONE IN

A Plan B Essay by Elise Levine

I bargained with God once—even wanted my poor mother—in a flooded cave in central Florida. Let me out. Let me finish my book. For about three electric seconds the fanged rock through which I crawled yielded like warm flesh.

Another time, I got lost inside a shipwreck, in the North Channel between Lakes Superior and Huron. I'd just finished ratcheting myself up the steel staircase from the engine room where my breath exhaust dislodged ferrous debris the size of poker chips. My boyfriend was still down. I hung around a few minutes. And then, craving still more sights, trained and equipped to solo—and probably a little stoned from the narcotic effects of nitrogen in the tanks of air I was breathing at this depth, under such pressure—I swam farther in.

A peep show of tiny rooms lined a narrow corridor. An ochre-stained sink. An upright rubber boot overflowing with mud. Levitating in the frigid water, I reached out to steady myself against a door jamb and by accident palmed a mud puppy, a type of aquatic salamander, unusual but not unheard of in these realms. Illumined by the powerful light I carried: blunt antediluvian head, star-cold eye regarding me back. *Enchanté*, brilliant alien. Even the wreck itself, this steel and wood cage, seemed a living organism, host to what lay secreted away in a habitual dark but for my awed presence.

I poked about some more. Such transport. Until a startled lingcod or a compromised beam or strut or my brass-tacks partner, aggrieved by my dilatory sightseeing—how increasingly we'd squabbled over dive plans—sent me ass over teakettle through the silt and I trashed the viz.

Once I settled—blindly figured floor from ceiling, understood *alive, still breathing*—shame struck. Profound fear—that too. But what clawed me most was this: despite my geeked-out multiplicities of life-sustaining gear, hard-won regimens of independence, insurgent belief in accomplishments, including my first book published and second project begun, here—inside a remote labyrinth—I'd fucked up.

In truth, I knew. So much for my prideful mask of self-invention. Like my mother, who'd succumbed for much of her adult life to chemical cocktails, I, too, foundered in the poisons of an abusive relationship, emotional treachery, deceit. Self-deceit. The smudged interior was me.

Somehow I bellied down, remembered to just basically breathe. And in soul-sucking blackness—possessed, for reasons still unfathomable to me, of sheer dumbass luck—on hands and knees I wormed my way out.

For a while I had it all figured. This writing thing, diving thing—snakes entwined in a transfiguring codependence. An Orphic conception that drove me to abandon my editorial day job and stay up all night excavating language, character, story. A swashbuckling idea I'd previously been too afraid to possess but which, unleashed, raced me to deep-drunk dives where I actually heard the blood blipping through my body, its arterial channels spiked with siren-call. To a state where I could fancy that narcosis brume as mist on the estuarial fields of the mind. To continue to dive even for a little longer after that close call in the wreck. Writing, diving: in both, I pushed back the darkness, emerged transformed.

And then I quit diving. Big duh: closer calls, not much left with which to bargain.

I reasoned. Maybe writing held its own as worthy exploration. Might require more of me, might require—well, me. Shorn of its partner, writing might be heartsick for a time, but it—and I—might survive.

And then damned if that second book didn't chew me over for years before finally spitting me free.

On one of my last-ever underwater excursions, I met a wolf eel. This encounter materialized in the Pacific, off British Columbia's Sunshine Coast. Apparently, the creature took one look at me and, teeth bared, bolted partway from its hiding hole between two submerged boulders to derrick back and forth. Like an endless revising of the distance between us, we bobbed, staring each other down until—in a non-navigable agon of exalted fascination and wincing, apologetic voyeurism—I finally moved on. But, god, what a mug. Wizened, ferocious. Scared—that I clearly divined. Thrilling to witness, and yet I felt bad, still do, for stressing her so far out.

Elise Levine is the author of a story collection, Driving Men Mad *(McClelland & Stewart, 2003), and a novel,* Requests and Dedications *(McClelland & Stewart, 2005). Her work has appeared in publications including* Hotel Amerika, Joyland: A Hub for Fiction, Sententia, Prairie Schooner, *and* Best Canadian Stories. *She lives in Baltimore, Maryland.*

THE BREEZE IN THE INK PAINTING
A Look2 Essay on Kawabata Yasunari
by Robert Anthony Siegel

It always seems wrong to me that Kawabata Yasunari's strange and wonderful fiction is left out of the ongoing conversation about the future of the novel. The debate in the U.S. is often framed in terms of fiction vs. nonfiction (David Shields, Sheila Heti), or realistic vs. metafiction (Jonathan Franzen, David Foster Wallace, Milan Kundera, and many others), but the Japanese Kawabata—who won the Nobel Prize in 1968 and died in 1972—comes at the problem from a different angle. His psychologically acute novels are written something like short stories, with the short story's emphasis on imagery and perception as the conduits of meaning. The result is realistic fiction relatively free of the cumbersome stage mechanics that we typically associate with realism. Swift, nimble, and intuitive, Kawabata's work has the power to surprise and discomfort.

Kawabata's realism focuses on the private, rather than the social and the political. Although he lived through some of the most tumultuous years in Japanese history, including the Pacific War and the U.S. Occupation, those events reverberate only faintly in his fiction, which keeps a tight focus on the interior lives of his characters. The typical Kawabata protagonist exists at a remove from other people, both yearning for and frightened of direct emotional connection. He is an observer, an aesthete, and an intellectual, suffocating under protective layers of irony and self-loathing, which inevitably masquerade as self-regard. Kawabata called them "orphans."

Kawabata was an orphan himself. Born in 1899 to a prosperous family living in Osaka, he lost both parents by the age of four, went to live with his paternal grandparents, and then lost both of them by the time he was sixteen. He entered Tokyo Imperial University in 1917 and was soon active in avant-garde artistic circles, participating in a literary movement, the New Perceptionists, that espoused a jumbled, secondhand version of Modernism, gleaned from Western sources.

The importance of this early affiliation for the development of Kawabata's work was twofold. First, it was an art-for-art's-sake stance at a time when "proletarian" writers practicing politically engaged fiction dominated the Japanese literary scene. Second, the movement's interest in capturing the physical world through a fresh, inventive use of language pointed Kawabata back toward classical Japanese writing, particularly the haiku tradition, with its focus on the image. The related form of *haikai-no-renga,* or linked verse, with its long, associative chains of images, gave him the hint he needed: the typical Kawabata novel is a series of short, intense scenes, largely free of authorial explanation and separated by white space. These scenes move back and forth through time in response to the shifting emotions of his protagonist, describing what ultimately feels more like a psychological journey than a plot in the usual sense.

The fiction that results is shot through with paradoxes. It deemphasizes plot, but nevertheless feels taut. The writing is spare, but also lyrical, full of exact renderings of the physical world and sensory experience. Kawabata's quiet, watchful protagonists do little, but are nevertheless intensely present. Their chilly sensibilities permeate the narrative voice, but the books themselves turn that emotional absence into its opposite: a hunger for feeling.

In "The Izu Dancer" (*Izu no odoriko*), a long story written in 1926 when Kawabata was just twenty-seven, his themes and style converge with complete success for the first time. A college student, backpacking in the country during a school vacation, falls in with a band of itinerant performers and gets a glimpse of what human connection might feel like. In particular, he experiences a tentative, mixed-up infatuation with the dancer of the title, moved both by her innocence and her vulnerability. The entertainers are vagabonds, walking from inn to inn with their instruments on their backs, and the dancer, who is just fourteen, performs for tips in front of drunken parties of male vacationers. She and the narrator make an affecting pair: the dancer at the social, and the narrator at the emotional, margins of life, bound for a brief interlude through mutual need. The story is suffused with the fleeting quality of human affections—what traditional Japanese aesthetics calls *mono-no-aware:* "the sadness of things."

Told in a deceptively simple first-person narration, the story's tone is softer, its narrative stance less unsettling, than Kawabata's later work.

It made him famous, and it is easy to imagine a lesser artist working within its parameters for the rest of his career, writing restrained,
lyrical stories about the possibilities and limits of love. But Kawabata
continued to grow in subversive directions. The novel *Snow Country*
(*Yukiguni*), published in pieces from 1935 to 1937, with a new ending
added in 1947, takes a similar situation and turns it into something
dark and ironic that resists easy epiphany.

   Snow Country's protagonist is Shimamura, a wealthy middle-aged
dilettante who resembles a "superfluous man" out of nineteenth-
century Russian literature—pretending to be amused by his own
uselessness while secretly frightened by his emotional emptiness.
The dilemma is deftly summed up in Shimamura's whimsical, self-
mocking career writing about the ballet, something he does despite
having never actually seen one (this is prewar Japan, after all, still
largely isolated from the West).

   At the opening of the story it is winter, and Shimamura has
returned to a hot-spring resort in the mountains north of Tokyo—
snow country—in search of Komako, a woman with whom he had
a brief affair during his last visit. But rather than falling in love, as
he half hopes, he spends his time watching her in a distanced,
aestheticized way, nervously registering her effect on him.

   Komako is as open as Shimamura is closed, as desperate to connect
as he is frightened to feel. In his absence, she has sold herself as a geisha
to pay the medical bills for her music teacher's son, who is dying. That
act of self-sacrifice has trapped her in the village, with no prospect but
"going quietly to seed in the mountains," serving as a glorified call girl
for the male vacationers who pass through. Utterly alone, she lives in
the attic of a farmhouse where silkworm cocoons were once stored,
reading by candlelight for glimpses of the outside world she will never
be a part of. In a series of notebooks she writes the plots of everything
she reads, all the characters and their connections, but nothing of her
own thoughts or opinions. She is only twenty.

   The reader hopes that Shimamura will rescue her, or that they will
rescue each other, even as time passes and the possibility becomes
more and more remote:

> *He had stayed so long that one might wonder whether he had*
> *forgotten his wife and children. He stayed not because he could*

not leave Komako nor because he did not want to. He had simply fallen into the habit of waiting for those frequent visits. And the more continuous the assault became, the more he began to wonder what was lacking in him, what kept him from living as completely. He stood gazing at his own coldness, so to speak. He could not understand how she had so lost herself. All of Komako came to him, but it seemed that nothing went out from him to her. He heard in his chest, like snow piling up, the sound of Komako, an echo beating against empty walls.

And then comes one of those great Kawabata moments, when the act of perception becomes plot:

The innkeeper had lent him an old Kyoto teakettle, skillfully inlaid in silver with flowers and birds, and from it came the sound of wind in the pines. He could make out two pine breezes, as a matter of fact, a near one and a far one. Just beyond the far breeze he heard faintly the tinkling of a bell. He put his ear to the kettle and listened. Far away, where the bell tinkled on, he suddenly saw Komako's feet, tripping in time with the bell. He drew back. The time had come to leave.

As a reader, I always find myself rebelling against the quiet ease with which Shimamura makes his choice, even as I feel, somehow, implicated in his callousness. And of course, that is the beauty of Kawabata's decision to make Shimamura his point-of-view character, rather than the brave and passionate Komako. The result is something powerful: a chilly, cerebral story about the inability to love that is also an argument for the importance of love.

There seems to have been an actual holiday trip to Izu behind "The Izu Dancer," and a real hot-spring resort (Yuzawa in Niigata prefecture), and a real *onsen geisha* at the heart of *Snow Country*. Literary pilgrims travel to both places nowadays, where they are met by plaques and statues. But the relationship between life and fiction is complex in the case of such a deeply imaginative writer. "Shimamura is not me," Kawabata wrote in an afterword to a later edition of the novel. "I am more Komako than Shimamura." The reader has no choice but to believe the truth of this assertion, given how vibrantly Komako inhabits the page, even as other autobiographical statements stress Kawabata's affinity with Shimamura:

I have the feeling that I have never taken a woman's hand in mine with romantic intentions. Some women may accuse me of lying, but it is my impression that this is not a mere figure of speech. And it is not only women that I have never taken by the hand. I wonder if it isn't true of life itself, as far as I'm concerned.

Kawabata is, in fact, fully present in both characters; much of the novel's strange force comes from the way it leaves us suspended between these two sides of him, with the tension between Komako and Shimamura, emotional need and psychological distance, fundamentally unresolved. This approach feels thoroughly modernist to the Western reader—think of the way Nabokov balances Kinbote and Shade in *Pale Fire*. But it is also natural to the haiku tradition on which Kawabata drew. Haiku poets create a poem by placing two images side by side, making them resonate together through the white space, free of authorial comment. The traditional term for this effect is *yūgen,* or mystery, a wonderfully deep, historically layered concept that invites endless elaboration, but in practice means two things: eschewing interpretation in favor of physical detail and image, and avoiding direct statement in favor of suggestion and subtext.

Both techniques are crucial to Kawabata's art, but the importance of yūgen is still larger, tied up with the idea of silence, or wordlessness, and the Buddhist concept of emptiness, or the insubstantial nature of phenomenon. "Truth is in the discarding of words," Kawabata writes in his 1968 Nobel essay, "Japan, the Beautiful and Myself," and while this may seem like an odd tack for a writer to take, it actually places him within the mainstream of traditional Japanese poetics. He follows the remark with a poem by Ikkyū, a Zen monk of the fourteenth century:

And what is it, the heart?
It is the sound of the pine breeze in the ink painting

The poem presents a densely packed paradox: the heart, the direct, intuitive grasp of the world's meaning, is nothing but the sound of the wind in the pine—even though the pine itself is nothing but an illusion, and therefore, by necessity, silent, without meaning. It is a lovely statement on the conundrum of consciousness, but it also puts one in mind of that scene in *Snow Country* with Shimamura in his room at the inn, listening to the steam in a teakettle imitate the wind in the pines as he decides that his affair with Komako is over. Kawabata may have revered Ikkyū, but he was also thoroughly modern, willing to shift the angle of vision and complicate the conclusion.

After finishing the bulk of *Snow Country* in 1937, Kawabata's output of fiction slowed. Working as a reporter, he covered the championship match that would become the basis of his novel *The Master of Go*, but didn't start work on the book till 1942, and didn't finish it till 1954. The extent to which this was an effect of the war years is hard to tell: his essays and magazine pieces got by the censors with minimal problems, and he was generally embraced by the authorities, joining a government-sponsored writers' organization dominated by right-wing cultural figures. But it's also true that he never succumbed to the aggressive chauvinism of his fellow members. For the most part, he stayed aloof from both politics and the disastrous events of the time, writing about the subjects that had always interested him. As he himself recalled in 1948:

> I am one of the Japanese who was affected least and suffered least because of the war...I did not experience any great inconvenience because of the war in either my artistic or my private life. And it goes without saying that I was never caught up in a surge of what is called divine possession to become a fanatical believer in or blind worshiper of Japan. I have always grieved for the Japanese with my own grief: that is all.

After the war, the idea of defeat as a threat to traditional Japanese culture was the link that connected him to the much younger novelist Mishima Yukio, whose career he helped foster in the postwar years. The two men were opposites as personalities and as writers: Mishima was an extrovert who liked celebrity, and his fiction is loaded with the kind of polemic and theorizing that Kawabata avoided in his own work. But they shared a vision of Japan's defeat as a crisis of meaning, and they both loathed the consumerist culture that was taking over the country.

Kawabata's sense of cultural crisis led him to take on a more public role after the war, becoming president of the Japanese chapter of PEN, and helping to found a publishing house. Nevertheless, there is no real break between his pre- and postwar fiction; it remains focused on the delicate exploration of self and eros, walled off from politics and recent history. *A Thousand Cranes* (*Senbazuru*), completed in 1949 and set in the rarefied world of the tea ceremony, traces a complicated love triangle between a young man, Kikuji, and his dead father's mistress and the mistress' daughter. The atmosphere is precisely observed and yet dreamy; people seem to overlap in a sort of double and triple exposure, and motives become wonderfully mixed, combining love and anger, hurt and longing over two generations. Kikuji's erotic obsession with his father's mistress, Mrs. Ota, hides a bewildered and bittersweet longing for his father, as well as anger over the pain his father caused his mother, who has also recently died. And while his attraction to Mrs. Ota's daughter, Fumiko, starts as a desire to break free from the past, it quickly circles back and becomes something darker and more ambivalent.

Throughout, Kawabata deftly mirrors the complex overlap between characters through the objects that surround them: the ancient, highly pedigreed ceramics used in the tea ceremony. After Mrs. Ota's death, when Fumiko brings Kikuji the Shino tea bowl that her mother used on trips with his father, he notices a spot of red coloring on the rim:

> *Where her mother's lipstick had sunk in?*
> *There was a red-black in the crackle too.*
> *The color of faded lipstick, the color of wilted red-rose, the color of old, dried blood—Kikuji began to feel queasy.*

Later, after they begin their own affair, Fumiko also gives him the Karatsu bowl used by his father when he was with Mrs. Ota. The bowl is "greenish with a touch of saffron and a touch too of carmine," and when they place it beside her mother's Shino, the effect is both eerie and seductive: "Seeing his father and Fumiko's mother in the bowls, Kikuji felt that they had raised two beautiful ghosts and placed them side by side." The reader also perceives what Kikuji cannot: that his relationship with Fumiko will never escape the shadow of the past because, on some level, he does not want it to. When Fumiko finally makes a bid for freedom by smashing the Shino, it is Kikuji who goes into the garden in search of the pieces.

The Western reader thinks of Freud at such moments, and it is true that Kawabata is a master of unexamined motives and the ways they shape both perception and choice. But the underlying worldview is Buddhist, not Freudian. The individual in Kawabata is a collection of shifting memories and intersecting longings, rather than a sharply defined entity with an independent existence. The boundaries between past and present, self and others, dream and reality, are always in flux in Kawabata's world. This gives *A Thousand Cranes* an eerie power that is different in feel from most Western novels devoted to the erotics of memory.

The Sound of the Mountain (*Yama no oto*), published in pieces between 1949 and 1954, benefits from this same approach to character, though it moves the action from the rarefied world of the tea ceremony to the more prosaic one of the suburban commuter.

Ogata Shingo is a well-to-do businessman who rides the train each day from his home in leafy Kamakura to his office in Tokyo. He's in his mid-sixties and starting to note the effects of old age—in particular, he's having problems with his memory—when one morning, before dawn, he hears a sort of low, indefinable roar coming from the mountain slope behind his house. This muted roar, what Shingo describes to himself as "the sound of the mountain," functions in the novel as a precursor of mortality, but also an expression of the world's elemental power, a vitality that transcends the limits of the individual, even as it finds expression through the individual's erotic longings.

The novel's foreground is devoted to Shingo's realization that he must let go of the memory of his wife Yasuko's sister, who died young, many years earlier, and whom he secretly loved. Small events at home or at the office circle around into memory, and memories trigger still older memories, which then circle back to the present. But the narrative always remains taut, driven by a quiet sense of urgency that derives from mortality itself—the sound of the mountain.

Typical of Kawabata's method is Shingo's recollection of his wedding: at the moment that he and his wife, Yasuko, are exchanging the ritual cups of *sake,* he notices a chestnut fall from a tree in the garden and is struck by how no one else seems to have seen it (a measure of his emotional remove from the ceremony, perhaps). He goes out to look for the chestnut later, thinking to show it to Yasuko, but finds himself unable to bring it up, constrained by the presence of his new brother-in-law, Yasuko's sister's widower, and all he represents:

The brother-in-law was a handsome man who quite outshone the bride. It seemed to Shingo that there was a peculiar radiance in his part of the room.

To Yasuko, her sister and brother-in-law were inhabitants of a dream world. In marrying her, Shingo had tacitly descended to her own lower rank.

He felt as if her brother-in-law were coldly looking down on the wedding from an elevation.

And the blank left by his failure to speak of so small a thing as the falling chestnut probably stayed on in their marriage.

The novel does its work through an associative chain of complex, layered moments like the one above; plot is relegated to the background. The tone is hopeful, in a bittersweet, autumnal way: whatever errors of omission Shingo may have been guilty of in the past, he finds his voice at key moments in the present, and we can feel his life shifting ever so gently into a new balance based on acceptance—his ability to listen to the sound of the mountain.

Kawabata seems not to have found the measure of peace he gave to Shingo: he committed suicide in 1972, at the age of 73. Because no note was found, speculation has varied. He was deeply affected by Mishima's very public suicide two years before, and claimed to have nightmares about him; he had health problems; he was not publishing; he was overwhelmed by his public role as an international spokesman for Japanese art and culture. But the story is inevitably more complicated; his Nobel essay, written four years before his death, already couples the idea of suicide to the artist's task, quoting with apparent approval the acclaimed writer and suicide Akutagawa Ryūnosuke:

I am living in a world of morbid nerves, clear and cold as ice...I do not know when I will summon up the resolve to kill myself. But nature is for me more beautiful than it has ever been before. I have no doubt that you will laugh at the contradiction, for here I love nature even when I am contemplating suicide. But nature is beautiful because it comes to my eyes in their last extremity.

Kawabata then goes on to mention a friend of his, a painter who also thought of killing himself: "He seems to have said over and over that there is no art superior to death, that to die is to live." The connections here are familiar: imminent death and heightened sensitivity, silence as a form of meaning that transcends words. At the end of his life, Kawabata seems to have arrived at the extreme pole of yūgen, where complete silence is the only complete art.

And yet Kawabata's work is, in fact, too rich to reduce to an aphorism on art and death. *House of the Sleeping Beauties* (*Nemureru bijo*), written in 1961, can perhaps illuminate the complexity of the situation, especially when placed next to *The Sound of the Mountain*. Both novels explore issues of mortality, but while the earlier book reaches for a sense of peace, steeped in mono-no-aware, *Sleeping Beauties* feels like something else again: a cry of primal rage.

The novel is almost Beckettian in its simplicity: the elderly Eguchi has been introduced to a sort of sexless fetish house in which rich old men pay to sleep beside beautiful young women in a chaste embrace. The women have been drugged, so there is no fear of their waking, and the men are free to gaze at their naked bodies in complete privacy, and then to take the tranquilizers that have been provided by the house and sleep next to them. Not sex, but a deep, restorative sleep is the point (an especially interesting detail, given that Kawabata himself was addicted to sleeping pills during this period).

The entire novel takes place within the confines of this house over a series of visits in which Eguchi watches a woman—always a different woman—shift and dream beside him. The women are described in precise, evocative detail until they become numinous presences inside the darkened bedroom: distinct in their personalities, brimming with the vitality of life, and yet dead to the world. They are, of course, empty mirrors for Eguchi's erotic longings, but they are also aggressively *present,* in the way that a cliff or a river is present, and they push back against his desire for imaginative control, insinuating the essential truth of his powerlessness. The experience of lying beside them is thus both seductive and maddening.

Much of the novel takes place in Eguchi's memory, and thus resembles *The Sound of the Mountain* in its richly associative construction. Once again, we get the shape of a life through a man's memories of women. But there is a difference: Eguchi's view of the sexes is darker and colder than

Shingo's, tinged with something that verges on the predatory, and his sense of isolation and personal emptiness is that much greater. The real connection is to *Snow Country*: Eguchi is Shimamura in old age, once again taking refuge in erotic connoisseurship, and Kawabata is playing the same sort of double game, forcing us to see out of the eyes of an emotionally closed narrator, drowning in his own egotism and terrified of dying alone. The crucial difference is that there is no Komako this time, making the counterargument on behalf of human connection. The end result is horror rather than sorrow. Mishima, an astute critic, likened the book to "a submarine in which people are trapped and the air is gradually disappearing."

Sleeping Beauties is an uncompromising novel, and it must have taken the author to the limit of his psychological endurance. I'm reminded of his Nobel essay once again, where he quotes the poet-monk Ikkyū: "It is easy to enter the realm of the Buddhas; it is hard to enter the realm of demons." Kawabata continues:

Much drawn to these words, I frequently make use of them when asked for a specimen of my calligraphy. They can be read in any number of ways, as difficult as one chooses...For the artist searching for truth, goodness and beauty, the desire and the fear aroused by "The demon realm is hard to enter," becomes like a prayer—with the inevitability of fate, either apparent on the surface of things, or hidden behind. There can be no realm of the Buddhas without the realm of demons. And the realm of demons is the realm that is difficult to enter.

In this realm, the artist takes all the deepest risks, going where he is afraid to go. "Not for the weak of heart," says Kawabata, and his own work testifies to his fearlessness in exploring both realms.

While Kawabata's legacy in Japan is assured, his readership in the U.S. seems to be limited to a niche audience of Japanese fiction lovers, despite the availability of good English translations (Kawabata's exquisite prose is dimmed in translation, but not erased). That situation will not readily change, given the American reader's general reluctance to embrace foreign writers. But in this moment of uncertainty about the future of the novel, Kawabata's ability to write powerful realistic fiction without the cumbersome trappings of realism—haiku fiction—gives him a new kind of relevance. So does his brave exploration of the erotics of perception, meaning, memory, and silence. My hope is that globalization has made us more willing to listen to voices from outside, and that his audience expands to include everyone interested in the expressive possibilities of the novel.

Robert Anthony Siegel's stories and essays have appeared or are forthcoming in Tin House, The Oxford American, Tablet, The Los Angeles Times Online, Story, The Harvard Review, Pushcart Prize 2012, *and elsewhere. He is the author of two novels,* All Will Be Revealed *(MacAdam/Cage, 2007), and* All the Money in the World *(Random House, 1997). He will be a Fulbright Fellow at Tunghai University in Taiwan from the fall of 2013.*

Contest Results · Awards · Fall 2013

Emerging Writer's Contest   Since 1971, Ploughshares has been committed to promoting the work of up-and-coming writers. This is the third year of our Emerging Writer's Contest, and our second accepting submissions in all three genres—poetry, nonfiction, and fiction. We are pleased to announce the following winners and runners-up. The winners will each receive $1,000 and be published in the staff-edited Winter 2013-14 issue.

FICTION
Winner: Memory Blake Peebles, "The Sugar Bowl"

First Runner Up: Randi Beck, "By Morning, New Mercies"
Second Runner Up: Jai Chakrabarti, "Lilavati's Fire"

POETRY
Winner: Josephine Yu: "Never Trust a Poem that Begins with a Dream" and "Narcissist Revises Tidal Theory"

First Runner Up: Brian Tierney: "A Necklace of Bones Made Out of Birds," "The Schopenhauer Elegy, or Like the Sokushinbutsu," "Trying to Remember," and "Waiting On a Word From The Mines"
Second Runner Up: Elizabeth Langemak: "Blue Hole," "Knowing and Not Knowing," "What Happens Next," "No Song," and "Also: A Definition"

NONFICTION
Winner: Mary Winsor, "Rock-a-bye, Ute"

First Runner Up (tie): Nathan Deuel, "This Means War"
First Runner Up (tie): Lisa K. Buchanan, "A Bedtime Story From Your Future"
Second Runner Up: Dorothy Bouzouma, "Zahna"

Many thanks to all of the authors for sharing their work with us. The Emerging Writer's Contest is open to all writers who have yet to publish a book, including chapbooks, eBooks, and self-published works. The contest is open for submissions from March 1 to May 15. Please visit our website (pshares.org) for guidelines.

Awards Our congratulations to the following *Ploughshares* writers, whose work has been selected for these anthologies:

Best Stories Jamie Quatro's story "Sinkhole," from the Spring 2012 issue edited by Nick Flynn, will appear in *O. Henry Prize Stories 2013*, selected by a prize jury of Lauren Groff, Edith Pearlman, and Jim Shepard. The anthology is due out September 2013, with Laura Furman as the series editor.

Best Essays Charles Baxter's essay, "What Happens in Hell," from the Fall 2012 issue edited by Patricia Hampl, has been selected for *The Best American Essays 2013*. The anthology is due out October 2013, with Cheryl Strayed as the guest editor and Robert Atwan as the series editor.

Pushcart Eric Fair's essay "Consequence" and Claudia Rankine's poem "Excerpt from *That Once Were Beautiful Children*," which both appeared in the Spring 2012 issue edited by Nick Flynn, and Charles Baxter's essay, "What Happens in Hell," from the Fall 2012 issue edited by Patricia Hampl, have been selected for *The Pushcart Prize XXXVIII: Best of the Small Presses*, which is due out November 2013 from Bill Henderson's Pushcart Press.

*Book Recommendations from
Our Advisory Editors*

Robert Boswell recommends *Make It, Take It* by Rus Bradburd: "A very effective novel in stories that looks at the underbelly of college basketball." (Cinco Puntos Press, January 2013)

DeWitt Henry recommends *What's Been Happening to Jane Austen?* by William H. Pritchard: "This volume collects his essays and reviews on Novelists and Novels, and on Critics and Criticism, in both cases ranging from classics to contemporaries. Whether or not his favorite books are yours, his forthrightness and standards are bracing. 'I continue to review,' he writes, 'because it helps to give a shape to my life.'" (The Impress Group, April 2011)

Maxine Kumin recommends *A Million Years with You: A Memoir of Life Observed* by Elizabeth Marshall Thomas: "Thomas is a keen observer of lions, hyenas, wild wolves, politics, religion, and society in Africa. She interweaves all of this with her personal history to form a memoir of extraordinary power." (Houghton Mifflin Harcourt, June 2013)

Philip Levine recommends *The Lives of Birds* by C. G. Hanzlicek: "How do you write about a life, your own, that is not spectacular? No suicides, no murderous cousins or brothers in the slammer, no years at war with anything more powerful than snails or aphids or old age, no poverty & no riches besides the pleasures available to us all, breathing, strolling, listening, sharing what we have with others & taking what's given; how can you make poetry out of that? If you'd like to learn how it's done, read C. G. Hanzlicek; he makes it seem so easy, but then the best poetry always seems easy. He can get more out of listening to a mockingbird than I can get out of all of Mahler, & as a bonus he can also get a lot out of Mahler. He's written the sweetest, most benign confessional poem I've ever read—it's titled 'Confessional Poem,' so you won't miss it. And don't miss 'The Recipe,' 'Alarm,' 'Seventeen,' 'My Father's Grave,' or the powerful title poem, or the squirrels 'up to their nuts in pecans.' Hanzlicek has such a quiet wit it pays to read his poems carefully, & though he can write 'Sometimes redemption glides down / In the form of mallards,' he never, ever strains to be important or wise." (Tebot Bach, April 2013)

Robert Pinsky recommends *New and Selected Poems: 1962-2012* by Charles Simic: "A source of pleasure and inspiration, wonderful to dip into at random." (Houghton Mifflin Harcourt, March 2013)

Dan Wakefield recommends *Boat Girl: A Memoir of Youth, Love, and Fiberglass* by Melanie Neale: "A memoir about a young woman being raised and homeschooled on a boat in the Caribbean. Finely and honestly observed." (Beating Windward Press, October 2012)

EDITORS' CORNER
New Works by Our
Advisory Editors

Frank Bidart, *Metaphysical Dog:*
Poems (Farrar, Straus and Giroux,
April 2013)

Robert Boswell, *Tumbledown: A*
Novel (Graywolf, August 2013)

Gish Jen, *Tiger Writing: Art, Culture,*
and the Interdependent Self (Harvard
University Press, March 2013)

Jay Neugeboren (with Michael B.
Friedman and Lloyd I.
Sederer), *The*
Diagnostic Manual of Mishegas, a
parody (CreateSpace, April 2013)

Carl Phillips, *Silverchest: Poems*
(Farrar, Straus & Giroux, April 2013)

Robert Pinsky, ed. with David
Lehman, *Best of the Best American*
Poetry: 25th Anniversary Edition
(Scribner, April 2013)

Robert Pinsky, *Singing School: Learn-*
ing to Write (and Read) Poetry by
Studying the Masters (W. W. Norton,
August 2013)

Lloyd Schwartz, *Music In—and On—*
the Air (Arrowsmith/PFP, April 2013)

Charles Simic, *New and Selected*
Poems: 1962–2012 (Houghton Mifflin
Harcourt, March 2013)

Elizabeth Strout, *The Burgess Boys: A*
Novel (Random House, March 2013)

Dan Wakefield, ed., *If This Isn't Nice,*
What Is?: Advice for the Young from
Kurt Vonnegut (RosettaBooks, April
2013)

CONTRIBUTORS' NOTES
Fall 2013

Sarah Shun-lien Bynum is the
author of two novels, both from
Houghton Mifflin Harcourt: *Ms.*
Hempel Chronicles, a finalist for the
2009 PEN/Faulkner Award; and
Madeleine Is Sleeping, a finalist for
the 2004 National Book Award. She
lives in Los Angeles and teaches in
the Graduate Writing Program at
Otis College of Art and Design.

Nick Dybek is a graduate of the
University of Michigan and the Iowa
Writers' Workshop. He's the author
of the novel *When Captain Flint Was*
Still a Good Man (Riverhead), winner of the 2013 Society of Midland
Authors Award. He's also a recipient
of a Granta New Voices selection,
a Michener-Copernicus Society of
America Award, and a Maytag Fel-
lowship. He lives in New York City.

Stuart Dybek, a former guest editor
for *Ploughshares,* is the author of
three books of fiction and two books
of poetry. Two new collections of his
fiction are scheduled to be published
by Farrar, Straus & Giroux in Spring
2014. "Misterioso," the short piece in
this issue, will appear in one of the
upcoming books.

Carolyn Ferrell received the *Plough-*
shares John C. Zacharis First Book
Award in 1997 for her collection
Don't Erase Me (Houghton Mifflin).
Her work has appeared in *Story,*
Ecotone, The New York Times, and
elsewhere; "Proper Library," a story
first published in *Ploughshares,* was
anthologized in *The Best American*

Short Stories of the Century (Mariner, 2000). Ferrell currently teaches at Sarah Lawrence College and is at work on another collection.

V.V. Ganeshananthan is the Zell Visiting Professor of Creative Writing at the University of Michigan. Her debut novel, *Love Marriage* (Random House), was long-listed for the Orange Prize and named one of *The Washington Post* Book World's Best of 2008. Her work has appeared in *Granta, The Atlantic, The Washington Post, Columbia Journalism Review, San Francisco Chronicle,* and *Unstuck,* among other publications. A recipient of fellowships from Yaddo, the Mac-Dowell Colony, and Phillips Exeter, she is at work on a second novel.

Travis Holland is the author of *The Archivist's Story* (The Dial Press, 2007). He is a recipient of the VCU Cabell First Novelist Award. His stories have previously appeared in *Ploughshares, Glimmer Train, and Five Points,* among other publications. A contributing editor for *Fiction Writers Review,* he lives and teaches in Ann Arbor, Michigan.

Michael Knight is the author of two novels (*Divining Rod* and *The Typist,* 1998 and 2010), two collections of short stories (*Goodnight, Nobody* and *Dogfight and Other Stories,* 2003 and 2007), and a collection of novellas (*The Holiday Season,* 2007), all currently in print from Grove/Atlantic. He teaches creative writing at the University of Tennessee.

Jo Lloyd's short stories have appeared in *The Best British Short Stories 2012* (Salt), *Southwest Review, Meridian,*

Riptide, and elsewhere. She has won the Asham Short Story Award, the Willesden Herald International Short Story Prize, and a McGinnis-Ritchie Award. Brought up in Wales, she currently lives in Oxford.

Megan Anderegg Malone was raised in Michigan's Upper Peninsula. She received her MFA from Bennington College, and her short fiction has appeared in *The Kenyon Review* and on National Public Radio. She lives with her husband and two redheaded daughters in Sonoma County, California, where she is at work on a novel. She can be reached at meg@maloneweb.com.

Jerry McGahan, 70, is a retired beekeeper and lives with his wife in Arlee, Montana, where he writes short fiction and novels, gardens, and paints. *The Georgia Review, The Iowa Review, The Antioch Review, The Gettysburg Review,* and a number of other literary journals have also accepted his stories. He has published a novel, *A Condor Brings the Sun,* with Sierra Club Books (1996). His paintings can be seen on jerrymcgahan.com.

Nancy Welch is a Professor of English at the University of Vermont. Her stories have appeared in *Prairie Schooner, The Threepenny Review,* and *The Greensboro Review,* among other journals, and her short-story collection, *The Road from Prosperity,* was published by Southern Methodist University Press in 2005.

GUEST EDITOR POLICY

Ploughshares is published three times a year: mixed issues of poetry and prose in the spring and winter and a prose issue in the fall. The spring and fall issues are guest-edited by different writers of prominence, and winter issues are staff-edited. Guest editors are invited to solicit up to half of their issues, with the other half selected from unsolicited manuscripts screened for them by staff editors. This guest editor policy is designed to introduce readers to different literary circles and tastes, and to offer a fuller representation of the range and diversity of contemporary letters than would be possible with a single editorship. Yet, at the same time, we expect every issue to reflect our overall standards of literary excellence.

SUBMISSION POLICIES

We welcome unsolicited manuscripts from June 1 to January 15 (postmark dates). We also accept submissions online. Please see our website (pshares.org) for more information and guidelines. All submissions postmarked from January 16 to May 31 will be recycled. From March 1 to May 15, we also accept submissions online for our Emerging Writer's Contest.

Our backlog is unpredictable, and staff editors ultimately have the responsibility of determining for which editor a work is most appropriate. If a manuscript is not timely for one issue, it will be considered for another. Unsolicited work sent directly to a guest editor's home or office will be ignored and discarded.

All mailed manuscripts and correspondence regarding submissions should be accompanied by a self-addressed, stamped envelope (s.a.s.e.). No replies will be given by e-mail (exceptions are made for international submissions). Expect three to five months for a decision. We now receive well over a thousand manuscripts a month.

For stories and essays that are significantly longer than 5,000 words, we are now accepting submissions for *Ploughshares Solos* (formerly *Pshares Singles*), which will be published as e-books. Pieces for this series, which can be either fiction or nonfiction, can stretch to novella length and range from 6,000 to 25,000 words. The series is edited by Ladette Randolph, *Ploughshares* editor-in-chief.

Simultaneous submissions are amenable as long as they are indicated as such and we are notified immediately upon acceptance elsewhere. We do not reprint previously published work. Translations are welcome if permission has been granted. We cannot be responsible for delay, loss, or damage. Payment is upon publication: $25/printed page, $50 minimum and $250 maximum per author, with two copies of the issue and a one-year subscription. For *Ploughshares Solos,* payment is $250 for long stories and $500 for work that is closer to a novella. The prize for our Emerging Writer's Contest is $1,000 for the winner in each genre: fiction, poetry, and nonfiction.

Dorothy Sargent Rosenberg Annual Poetry Prizes, 2013

*Prizes ranging from $1,000 up to as much as $25,000 will be awarded for the finest lyric poems celebrating the human spirit. The contest is open to all writers, published or unpublished, who will be under the age of 40 on November 6, 2013. Entries must be postmarked on or before the first Saturday in October (October 5, 2013). Only previously unpublished poems are eligible for prizes. Names of prize winners will be published on our website on February 5, 2014, together with a selection of the winning poems. Please visit our website **www.DorothyPrizes.org** for further information and to read poems by previous winners. **Please note that our deadline for entries is earlier than in previous years and that we have a new mailing address.***

<u>This is the last year of this competition in its present form.</u> We have donated our funds to the Poetry Foundation, where they will help support the newly established Ruth Lilly and Dorothy Sargent Rosenberg Poetry Prizes, beginning in 2014. Meanwhile, we are looking for some individual, group, or institution interested in carrying forward the Dorothy Prizes into the future, probably with less generous awards. Please see the invitation on our website and send us your proposals.

CHECKLIST OF CONTEST GUIDELINES FOR 2013

• Entries must be postmarked on or before October 5, 2013.

• Past winners may re-enter until their prizes total in excess of $25,000.

• All entrants must be under the age of 40 on November 6, 2013.

• Submissions must be original, previously unpublished, and in English: no translations, please.

• Each entrant may submit one to three separate poems.

• Only one of the poems may be more than thirty lines in length.

• Each poem must be printed on a separate sheet.

• Submit two copies of each entry with your name, address, phone number and email address clearly marked on each page of one copy only.

• Include an index card with your name, address, phone number and email address and the titles of each of your submitted poems.

• Include a $10 entry fee payable to the Dorothy Sargent Rosenberg Memorial Fund. (This fee is not required for entrants resident outside the U.S.A.)

• Poems will not be returned. Include a stamped addressed envelope if you wish us to acknowledge receipt of your entry.

Mail entries to:

Dorothy Sargent Rosenberg Poetry Prizes
PO Box 148
Stewarts Point, California 95480

$15,000 in Awards

23rd Annual Jeffrey E. Smith

EDITORS' PRIZE

$5,000 Fiction • $5,000 Poetry • $5,000 Essay

The Missouri Review is now accepting submissions for the 22nd Annual Jeffrey E. Smith Editors' Prize competition.

In addition to the $15,000 awarded to the first place winners, three finalists in each category receive cash awards and are considered for publication. Past winners have been reprinted in the *Best American* series.

Page Restrictions

Fiction and nonfiction entries should not exceed 25 typed, double-spaced pages. Poetry entries can include any number of poems up to 10 pages in total. Each story, essay, or group of poems constitutes one entry.

Entry Fee

$20 for each entry (checks made payable to *The Missouri Review*). Each fee includes a one-year subscription (digital or print!) to *The Missouri Review*. Please enclose a complete e-mail and mailing address.

Entry Instructions

Include the printable contest entry form (available online). On the first page of each submission, include author's name, address, e-mail and telephone number. Entries must be previously unpublished and will not be returned. Mark the outside of the envelope "Fiction," "Essay," or "Poetry." Each entry in a separate category must be mailed in a separate envelope. Enclose a #10 SASE or e-mail address for an announcement of winners.

Go Green: Enter Online!

We are also accepting electronic submissions. For details, go to *www. missourireview.com/contest*

Mailing Address

Missouri Review Editors' Prize
357 McReynolds Hall
University of Missouri
Columbia, MO 65211

The Missouri Review

Postmark Deadline October 1, 2013

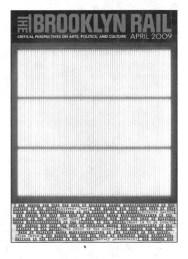

PLOUGHSHARES

Stories and poems for literary aficionados

Known for its compelling fiction and poetry, *Ploughshares* is widely regarded as one of America's most influential literary journals. Most issues are guest-edited by a different writer for a fresh, provocative slant—exploring personal visions, aesthetics, and literary circles—and contributors include both well-known and emerging writers. *Ploughshares* has become a premier proving ground for new talent, showcasing the early works of Sue Miller, Edward P. Jones, Tim O'Brien, and countless others. Past guest editors include Richard Ford, Raymond Carver, Derek Walcott, Tobias Wolff, Kathryn Harrison, and Lorrie Moore. This unique editorial format has made *Ploughshares* a dynamic anthology series—one that has established a tradition of quality and prescience. *Ploughshares* is published in April, August, and December, usually with a prose issue in the fall and mixed issues of poetry and fiction in the spring and winter. Inside each issue, you'll find not only great new stories, essays, and poems, but also a profile on the guest editor, book reviews, and miscellaneous notes about *Ploughshares*, its writers, and the literary world. Subscribe today.

Subscribe online at www.pshares.org.

- -